Monst

of myth and legend

Paul Groves

Nigel Grimshaw

Edward Arnold

First published 1977 by
Edward Arnold (Publishers) Ltd
41 Bedford Square, London WC1B 3DQ

Reprinted 1978, 1980

ISBN 0 7131 0096 6

Acknowledgements
Acknowledgement of each primary or secondary source consulted
for the better-known myths and legends would be lengthy, and
establishing the precise nature of our indebtedness to each would be
difficult. Where it has been possible to acknowledge our particular
debt to a specific source, we have done so in the text.

P. G., N. G.

Set in Photon 12/13 Times
Printed in Great Britain by
The Camelot Press Ltd, Southampton

Contents

A Note to the Teacher

These tales of some of the heroes of myth and legend and the varied monsters they confront have been retold in deliberately simple language, accessible to most children or suitable for reading aloud to remedial groups. Each story is accompanied by suggestions for work of relevance, though these are by no means all-inclusive, so that the book may be used by itself as part of an English course or as support for more wide-ranging or multi-disciplinary approaches. In any case, teachers are also at liberty to select from or expand on these work suggestions according to particular needs.

Answers at a simple level can practically always be given to the first section, 'Looking at the story again', by quoting a sentence or phrase from the text. The second section, 'Further questions', requires more thought and gives wider freedom of expression. The third, 'Things to do', while not exhausting the possibilities, contains suggestions for personal writing, drama, art and individual follow-up work in the library. With mixed-ability classes, for instance, different sections could be allotted to suit the level of ability of individuals or groups.

After reading these tales, children might be interested in making models of palaces, treasure, weapons and armour, costumes and the monsters themselves, but precise suggestions about these have not been included since facilities and opportunities for such work will not exist in every classroom. We would stress that even the questions given are points of departure to be developed as each actual teaching situation dictates.

In the Pronunciation Guide we have indicated stress by capital letters. Syllables which read like actual English words, e.g. 'owe' or 'ADD' are to be pronounced as such. Other syllables require standard English pronunciation.

A Few Words to Begin With

In myth we see mankind trying to explain the world to itself. It is a world in which man is not very powerful. The forces ruling over that world are mysterious, like the gods, and a man's strength, bravery and intelligence are of great value to him.

For the Greeks, their undying gods were rather like human beings. They could be jealous and revengeful. Sometimes they used their powers to assist a person; sometimes they used it to harm him. There were times when they seemed not to care about mankind and turned deaf ears to appeals for help. Certain individuals might have a god for a father. These exceptional people were not always fortunate, although they generally had god-like gifts of strength or courage or cleverness.

The word 'mythology' comes from two words in Greek which can be understood to mean 'story-telling'. In the beginning, these stories were told in speech. They were passed on that way, in talk, from the old to the young. Then they came to be written down and have been told and re-told in writing for very many centuries. It may be that some of these ancient stories originally were about real people but the truth of that can never be known.

The Minotaur

Theseus had two fathers; one was human and the other was a sea god. The fight with the Minotaur is only one of the adventures this hero had. We do not know whether Theseus ever really existed. But there are still the ruins of an immense palace to be seen at Knossos in Crete. Three thousand and more years ago, it must have been a splendid building with countless rooms and corridors. It would have been a bewildering place to find one's way about in. Was the palace itself the origin of the idea of a maze through which Theseus had to find his way?

Pronunciation Guide
The 'th' sound in Theseus is soft, as in the word 'thin'.
Theseus   THEE-see-us
The 'Min' in Minotaur is like the word 'win'
Minotaur   MIN-owe-tore
Ariadne   Arry-ADD-ny

One day, thousands of years ago, a ship sailed into a Cretan harbour. The sky was a clear blue and the sun was hot. Crowds had gathered to watch the ship come in. On deck stood seven young men and seven young women. All of them, except one, looked unhappy and afraid. The handsome young man who was smiling was Theseus. He was the son of the king of Athens.

Every year Athens had to send a sacrifice to king Minos of Crete. Every year Minos demanded seven young men and seven young women. They were given to the Minotaur to be killed.

The Minotaur was a monster, half-bull, half-giant. This bull-headed man lived in the Labyrinth. That was a place of many caves and passages. If you walked a hundred yards into the Labyrinth, you were lost. The passages twisted and turned; one led confusingly into another. Neither a torch nor a map could help you. You would walk and run until you could walk and run no more. Then you would simply have to wait. You would hear the roaring of the Minotaur coming closer and closer. You would know that there was no escape.

These young people on the deck of the ship knew what death awaited them. One by one they would be driven into the Labyrinth at spear point. One by one they would die on the savage horns of the Minotaur. And still Theseus was smiling.

Ariadne, the king's daughter, watched the ship come in from her palace window. The crowd shouted with cruel pleasure as the fourteen victims were brought ashore. But there was no look of pleasure on Ariadne's face and she called one of her maids to her.

'Princess?' asked the maid.

'The sacrifices.' Ariadne pointed. 'Year after year they have to come. It's terrible.'

'It's the order of the king,' said the maid.

'My own father! That makes it worse. And yet— the handsomest of them seems quite without fear. He's even smiling.'

'He won't be smiling when he meets the Minotaur,' said the maid.

'You heartless little animal!' Ariadne looked so fierce that the maid stepped back.

'I'm sorry, princess,' she stammered. 'I only meant——'

'Be quiet. Go and find out his name. Find out which prison they will be kept in. Go now!'

The maid, with a scared face, bowed and ran off to the harbour.

All the young women from Athens were put together in a dungeon under the palace and the young men were taken to another not far away. Both of the prisons were cut out of the rock and both were completely dark. Theseus tried to hearten his companions but without much success. For most of the time they sat silently in the darkness, though now and again one would sigh or another cry out. But their thoughts were fixed on what was waiting for them and they were too full of terror to speak. They were remembering, too, the families they had left behind in Athens for ever.

Theseus was also thinking of his father, the king. When Theseus had asked to be sent to Crete, the king had been horrified. It had taken all Theseus's arguments to get him to agree. If the Minotaur

were killed, Athens would no longer need to send the young people
as sacrifices. Theseus had talked so well that his father had finally let
him come. Until now he had felt hopeful. Now, in the dark, he was
not so sure. He had no weapons. And—if he did manage to kill the
monster—how would he get out of the Labyrinth again?

'Theseus!' It was a woman's voice and Theseus jumped. It had
come from outside the dungeon.

'Who's there?' he called sharply.

'Ssh! My name is Ariadne, daughter of King Minos.'

'What do you want?'

'A brave man. One who will try to kill the Minotaur. To stop these
yearly sacrifices.'

'Let me out,' said Theseus. 'I'll take that chance.'

He heard the key rattle in the lock and the door was opened. By
the light of the torch she carried, he could see that Ariadne was very
beautiful. Her maid was with her.

She warned them all to keep quiet and the other young men
followed Theseus out into the corridor.

'There is a boat ready in the harbour,' she told them. 'My maid
will help you to rescue the seven young women from their dungeon.
Then all of you must go down to the harbour and wait. Be careful
that you are not seen.' She turned to Theseus. 'Follow me,' she said.

She led him out of the prison and through the darkness of the night
until they reached the entrance to the Labyrinth. Ariadne handed
Theseus a sword.

'You'll need this, too,' she told him and gave him a ball of thread.

'Why?' he asked.

'It will help you to find your way out again,' she said. 'Tie the end
to one of the bushes near the entrance. Unwind the thread as you
go into the Labyrinth. Then you can follow it back when you come
out.'

He did as she advised and took the torch she gave him. Inside the
cave, it threw great flickering shadows on the walls. Moving
cautiously forward, he let the thread run out through his fingers.
Sudden breezes came at him from side passages, though the air soon
seemed thicker. The only sounds were the sputter of the blazing
torch, the occasional clink of his sword on stone and his footfalls on
the dusty rock.

Then he stopped dead. A savage sound had suddenly echoed through the caves ahead of him. It was like the bellowing of a bull but strangely human, too. Theseus took a deep breath and went on. The sound came again and he made his way towards it through the twisting passages. He stopped again when he saw a faint glow of light a good way ahead.

For a second, in the glow stood the Minotaur. It was huge, its head blunted and ugly with great, curving horns. It darted away down a side cavern. It was hunting him now.

With a firm grip on his sword and the torch held high, he went slowly on. Even so, he was not ready for its rush. It charged out at him from a gaping cave at his side, plunging at him with its horns.

Theseus leaped to one side and swung the sword but he was too slow. He missed completely and the tip of one horn slashed his side. The Minotaur came at him again and this time Theseus's stroke clanged harmlessly on the horns and the sword was knocked from his hand. He stuck the torch into a crack in the rock and dodged into the shadow.

The fierce eyes of the monster gleamed at him in the dark. The torch flame was dull and smoky. But it gave light enough for Theseus to see his danger. The great, muscled body of the Minotaur was that of a man but from its bull's mouth saliva dripped as it snorted and swung those long curving horns.

Theseus seized them and tried to twist the thick, hairy neck but the Minotaur threw him off easily and would have pinned him against the wall, if he had been slower to dodge. As it was, one horn caught his arm, drawing blood. He fought hard but his fists were no match for the strength of the Minotaur. It flung him back. He tripped and fell sprawling against the wall.

These horns were almost on him. Struggling to rise, he found the hilt of the sword, raised it and thrust. Luck was with him. It drove straight at the Minotaur's heart and with a roar the monster fell dead.

By the light of the torch he found the end of the thread and made his way through the Labyrinth to where Ariadne waited.

All had gone well at the harbour. His companions had not been seen and the ship was ready. The wind was in their favour and before long they were far out at sea bound for freedom. The power of Minos was broken. Never again would Athens send sacrifices to Crete.

Looking at the story again
1. What did the Minotaur look like?
2. What sort of place was the Labyrinth?
3. What did the crowd do when the victims were brought ashore?
4. Where were the young women from Athens put?
5. Who opened the door of Theseus's prison?
6. Why was Theseus given the ball of thread?
7. How was Theseus wounded?
8. How did he and his companions escape?

Further questions
1. When do you first know that Theseus is brave?
2. Another word for 'labyrinth' is m - - - .
3. Why was Ariadne not pleased to see the ship?
4. Why was she angry with her maid?
5. How might she have got the keys to the dungeon?
6. What reasons might she have had for helping Theseus?

Things to do
1. Draw the plan of a maze.
2. Theseus and his companions went from Athens in Greece to Heraklion in Crete. Draw a sketch map of their voyage.
3. Look at the picture and draw one of your own for this story.
4. What happened after Theseus and his companions left Crete? You can find this out from a book or make up your own story.
5. Find out what kind of clothes they wore or what kind of ships they sailed in and draw a picture.
6. Write out in play-form the argument Theseus might have had with his father, Aegeus, before he went to Crete.
7. Write an account of the story as if you were one of the young men or women who went with Theseus.
8. The story can be divided up like this:
    (a) Theseus persuades his father to let him go to Crete.
    (b) They arrive at the harbour.
    (c) They talk in the dungeon.
    (d) Ariadne lets them out and takes Theseus to the Labyrinth.
    (e) Theseus tracks down and kills the Minotaur.
    (f) They set sail for Athens.
  Act out part or all of the story.

The Gorgons

The full story of Perseus deals with the will of the gods. It was prophesied to Acrisius, the father of Danae, that his own grandson would kill him. Acrisius, therefore, shut Danae away in a tower for life. Zeus, ruler of the gods, visited her in the form of a shower of gold and became the father of Perseus. When Perseus was born, Acrisius set him and his mother afloat on the sea and hoped that he had seen the last of them both. But Perseus, after the adventures related in these stories, returned to the kingdom of Acrisius and the will of the gods was fulfilled. While competing in some games, Perseus threw a discus which struck Acrisius and accidentally killed him.

Pronunciation Guide

Acrisius	Ack-RIZZ-yooss	Medusa	Med-YOU-sa
Zeus	Zyooss	Dictys	DICK-tiss
Danae	DAN-eh-ee	Athena	Ath-EEN-a
Perseus	PURR-see-us	Hermes	HER-meez
Polydectes	Polly-DECK-teez	Hades	HAY-deez

Danae, together with her small son Perseus, had been cast out of her own country and they had arrived in the kingdom of the cruel Polydectes. Now, when Perseus had grown into a young man, Polydectes had decided that he wanted to marry Danae. But she did not care for him. He would have to marry her by force and he was afraid of what Perseus could do. His plan to get Perseus out of the way was soon formed.

Polydectes asked for a proof of loyalty from all the young men in his kingdom to be given to him on his birthday. On the day, each one brought him a gift except Perseus who had nothing to give.

'You've lived in my country all your life,' Polydectes sneered. 'And now you're too mean to be grateful. You've given me no sign of your loyalty. What am I going to do with you?'

'I have no possessions and no money,' Perseus said. 'I have only these two hands. But I'll get you your gift. Name it and you shall have it.'

Polydectes smiled at the proud and angry young man. The trap had worked.

'Get me the Gorgon's head,' he demanded.

There was dead silence in the crowded room. The Gorgons were three hideous monsters. A single look from the savage eyes of one of them turned any living thing to stone. One of them had once been a woman but she had offended the gods. They had made her terrible to see, like the others. Her hands were brass, her teeth were huge and piglike and she had writhing snakes instead of hair. Her name was Medusa.

For a long moment Perseus stared at Polydectes. Then, without a word he turned and left them all. Polydectes' smile grew broader. One way or another, he had seen the last of that dangerous young man. Now he could marry the mother, Danae, whether she liked it or not.

But Perseus had friends among the gods. He asked Dictys, another friend, to look after his mother and sought the help of Athena, the goddess of wisdom and Hermes, the messenger of the gods. Hermes gave him a sword. Athena gave him her shield, polished to the brightness of a mirror, and some good advice.

'The Gorgons are hard to find,' she told him. 'You will have to ask the Grey Sisters where they are. When you do find them, use my shield as a mirror. Never look directly at a Gorgon. Look at its reflection in the mirror as you cut off its head. Otherwise you will be turned to stone.'

'You will need more than a sword and a shield,' Hermes told him. 'You will first need to creep up on the Gorgons unseen. Then, a Gorgon's head loses none of its power in death and its blood is poisonous. If you succeed in beheading one, you will need a bag in which to carry the head. You cannot kill all three. You will be chased. And the Gorgons can fly far more swiftly than any man can run.'

'How can I best manage to do it, then?' asked Perseus.

'You must ask the Nymphs who live at the back of the North Wind,' Athena told him.

'And where can I find them?' called Perseus. The bright figures of the gods were already fading.

'The Grey Sisters know,' said Athena. Then she and Hermes vanished.

It was not easy to discover the Grey Sisters and they were not a pleasant sight when he did find them. There were three of them. They were already very old and they would live for ever. Their hair was thin and white; their faces were hideous and wrinkled. Most horribly, their gums were toothless and their eye-sockets were empty. Between the three of them they had only one eye and one tooth. They passed these from one to another when they wanted to see or to eat.

Perseus crept up on them and, as they passed the eye from hand to hand, he took it. When they discovered the loss, there was an outcry. It was easy for Perseus to make them tell him where he could find the Gorgons and the Nymphs at the back of the North Wind. He gave them back their eye and went on his way, followed by their curses.

He was relieved to find that the Nymphs at the back of the North Wind were quite unlike the Grey Sisters. The Nymphs were beautiful. They were even pleased to see the handsome young man. They gave Perseus a magic bag in which to carry the dreadful head of the Gorgon and a pair of winged sandals with which he could fly. One of the Nymphs was so taken with him that she dared to go down into the land of the dead to fetch him the Cap of Darkness that Hades, the king of the ghosts, kept there. Wearing that made a man invisible.

The Nymphs did not like letting Perseus go but he insisted. Even though he had magical weapons and magical powers, they did not like the idea of him facing the Gorgons alone.

When he saw the monsters, Perseus knew why the Nymphs had been afraid. He was careful to look only in his polished shield as he drew near. The snakes that grew on the heads of the Gorgons heard him coming and hissed to give the alarm.

The monsters had wings, their faces were broad and flat with hard, fierce eyes. Tusks grew out of their mouths instead of teeth. Perseus wore the cap that made him invisible but their piglike noses sniffed the air as he approached. Their metal hands clawed for him and they screeched like giant crows.

He hung back. He would have to dive in among those writhing

snakes, those teeth that looked like razors and the grabbing hands. And he would not be able to see what was going on around him or really where he was going. He would have to keep his eyes on the reflection in the mirror. But he had come too far to stop now.

Gathering his courage, he swooped on the middle one, guiding himself with the mirror. His sword swept, the Medusa's head flew from its body. In another moment, he had it safe in its magic bag and was making his escape.

The two other Gorgons could not see him but they had caught his scent and they gave chase. Back and forth across the sky they flew, screaming with rage and clawing the air. But the flying sandals of the Nymphs kept Perseus safe. Before long, he had left them behind and was on his way back to Greece.

Looking at the story again

1. Whose kingdom did Danae and Perseus arrive in?
2. What gift did Polydectes want Perseus to bring him?
3. Why were the Gorgons dangerous to look at?
4. What man helped Perseus? What two gods helped him?
5. Who told Perseus where he could find the Nymphs who live at the back of the North Wind?
6. What three things did the Nymphs give Perseus to help him in his task?
7. What grew on the Gorgons' heads instead of hair?
8. How did Perseus avoid looking directly at Medusa when he cut off her head?

Further questions

1. How much of a sign of loyalty is gift-giving?
2. What kind of a man was Polydectes?
3. Why did the room fall silent when Polydectes demanded the Gorgon's head?
4. Why was it necessary for Perseus to be invisible when he faced the Gorgons?
5. What is the usual purpose of a shield in fighting?
6. List all the things that made the Gorgons so dangerous.

7. What, in your opinion, was the thing most useful to Perseus and why?

Things to do
1. Write a story about someone who finds that he or she can fly.
2. Look at the picture and draw one of your own for this story.
3. Use a dictionary or encyclopaedia to find out what the Greeks meant by 'Nymphs'. What sort of nymph does a present day fisherman use?
4. Find out what you can about Hermes and Athena and write a description of both.
5. List all the gifts Perseus was given and say how each was useful to him.
6. Write a poem called 'The Evil Eye' or 'The Face in the Mirror'.
7. The story can be divided up like this:
    (a) Polydectes asks Perseus for the gift of the Gorgon's head.
    (b) Athena and Hermes appear to Perseus to help him.
    (c) Perseus plays his trick on the Grey Sisters.
    (d) Perseus visits the Nymphs.
    (e) Perseus attacks the Gorgons.
Act out all or part of the story.

The Sea Monster

Pronunciation Guide

Andromeda	An-DROM-edd-a
Cassiopoeia	Cassy-oh-PEA-a
Cepheus	SEFF-yuss
Phineus	FIN-yuss

While he was flying over the sea, Perseus saw far below him, walking along the shore, a crowd of people. He flew lower. At the head of the line was a beautiful girl. An older man and woman were with her.

When the crowd reached the sea, the girl was chained to a rock and the others hurried away as if in fear. Perseus flew down and took off the cap that made him invisible. The girl gave a little scream and stared at him in fear and surprise.

'Don't be afraid,' he told her. 'My name is Perseus.'

'You must get away from here,' she told him, looking even more frightened. 'You're in great danger.'

'Why are you chained to the rock?' he asked.

'I am to be sacrificed to the sea-monster. My name is Andromeda. My father is king Cepheus and my mother is queen Cassiopoeia. I am here by their orders.'

'Your parents have ordered the sacrifice!' Perseus was horrified.

'There was nothing else they could do,' Andromeda said. 'If there is no sacrifice, the monster will come up on the land and kill all he can.'

'We'll see about that,' Perseus told her grimly.

He had no time to say more. A bubbling roar split the air as the monster's head broke the surface of the sea near them. It was like a crocodile's but many times larger. The humps on its back stood out above the water. It looked to be about fifty yards long. Great waves arose on either side of the savage head as, with all its jagged teeth showing, it rushed towards the rock. Andromeda screamed again.

'Close your eyes,' Perseus ordered, 'and keep them closed.'

He shut his own and pulled the terrible head of the Gorgon from the magic bag. The roaring stopped suddenly. He put back the head into the bag and opened his eyes.

There was no longer a monster. Instead he saw a line of rocks not far off. The nearest one, rising high out of the water, looked like the head of a crocodile. There had been no need for him to warn Andromeda to close her eyes, for she had fainted. With his magic sword, he cut her chains and carried her back to her parents.

They were overjoyed to see her. Cassiopoeia wept tears of relief. Cepheus tried to thank Perseus but the words would not come at first. Perseus was very willing to stay at the court for a few days. He had seen at once how attractive Andromeda was and was fairly sure that she liked him, too.

Preparations were made for a feast to celebrate Andromeda's rescue. But it was not long before she and Perseus knew that they were in love with each other. Cepheus and Cassiopoeia eagerly agreed to the marriage and the celebration became a marriage feast as well.

It had only just begun when the doors of the hall were flung open. People jumped to their feet in alarm. It was the robber, Phineus, with all his men and they were heavily armed. No one in the hall had any weapons at all.

'What do you gang of murderers want here?' Cepheus demanded.

'All the wealth you have,' Phineus told him, 'and Andromeda for myself.'

Cepheus was about to speak but Perseus stopped him. He stepped forward so that he stood in front of Phineus and the robbers. His back was towards Cepheus and the other people at the feast.

'I give you fair warning, Phineus,' he said. 'Leave us in peace or you are all dead men.'

'Fool!' Phineus jeered. 'What will you fight with? Your bare hands? All of us? Stand aside.'

'Leave this hall,' said Perseus, 'or lose your life.'

'My life?' Phineus laughed harshly. 'You've lost yours.' And he swung his sword in a two-handed stroke at Perseus's head.

In the same instant Perseus turned his face aside and pulled out the Gorgon's head. All the time he had been in Cepheus's kingdom he had kept the magic bag with him. It was too dangerous to leave around.

Phineus's blow never fell. As Perseus replaced the head in its bag, there were no longer armed men at that end of the hall. There was only a line of stone figures. Phineus had become a statue with its stone sword raised.

Cepheus was very pleased to have his kingdom freed from Phineus's robber band, though a little sad that Perseus had to be on his way. He and Andromeda were given a swift ship and at last were back in Polydectes's country. Bad news greeted Perseus.

Danae had firmly refused to marry Polydectes. She had been put in prison and suffered all kinds of ill-treatment there. Dictys was in prison, too, for protecting her. The threat of death hung over both of them.

When Perseus walked into the hall of Polydectes, the cruel king turned pale. Then he saw that the young man had no weapons. All he carried was a leather bag. Polydectes looked round at all his armed men and laughed.

'So you have come creeping home again,' he said.

'I have brought you your gift,' Perseus told him.

'The Gorgon's head? You?' Polydectes laughed again. 'No man could do that and live.'

'I have done it.'

'Liar!'

'Let my mother go,' Perseus said.

'Are you threatening me?' Polydectes made a sign to his guards.

'Let her go or I will show you the Gorgon's stare!'

'Cut him to pieces!' Polydectes ordered and the guards drew their weapons.

Perseus flung open the bag and sent the dreadful head rolling on the table. Medusa's dead eyes were the last thing Polydectes saw.

Danae and Dictys were released from prison. Perseus returned the gifts of the Nymphs, Hermes' sword and Athena's shield to the gods. Athena had the head of Medusa placed in the centre of her shield.

Polydectes' people were so pleased to be rid of the cruel king and his evil soldiers that they made Perseus king instead. He and Andromeda reigned in the kingdom for many years.

Looking at the story again

1. Why was Andromeda chained to the rock?
2. What did the sea-monster's head look like?
3. How did Perseus kill it?
4. Who disturbed the marriage feast and what happened to him?
5. What had happened to Danae, while Perseus was away?
6. What happened to the magic shield and the sword? Where was Medusa's head put?
7. Who was made king after the death of Polydectes?

Further questions

1. Why had Andromeda's parents agreed to sacrifice her?
2. Why did Perseus tell her to close her eyes?
3. Why was Perseus in no hurry to get home?
4. What might have happened if Perseus had left the bag with the Gorgon's head in it lying around?
5. For what reason might Polydectes have turned pale when he first saw Perseus?
6. Was Perseus quite fair to Phineus and Polydectes?
7. Where would you have put the Medusa's head so that it could do no further harm?

Things to do

1. Was Polydectes a good king? List the things that would make a man a good king or a good leader.
2. Perseus started from one of the Greek islands. Draw a sketch map of his imaginary travels, labelling the places he might have visited and the beings he met.
3. Look at the picture and draw one of your own for this story.
4. Write a poem called 'Sea Dreams' or 'The Hero's Return'.
5. Find out what kinds of food might have been served at a marriage feast in those times.
6. The story can be divided up into several parts:
    (a) Perseus saves Andromeda.
    (b) Cepheus and Cassiopoeia thank him.
    (c) Phineus disturbs the marriage feast.
    (d) Perseus confronts Polydectes.
   Act out all or part of the story.

The Hydra

To the Greeks, Herakles was the best-known of all their heroes, with his great strength and courage. Some accounts say that he had the gift of healing. The story also goes that he founded the Olympic Games.

He died strangely, killed by the blood of a dead enemy. Believing the blood had magic powers helpful to Herakles, his wife dipped one of his tunics in it. When Herakles put the tunic on, the poison from the blood ate the flesh from his bones.

It is also said that he received a great reward for his labours. He was made immortal and given the honour of guarding for ever the gateway to the home of the Greek gods. Herakles is his Greek name; the Romans called him Hercules.

Pronunciation Guide

Hydra	HIDE-ra	Argolis	Are-GO-liss
Hera	HE-ra	Eurystheus	You're-ISS-thyuss
Herakles	H(E)R-ack-leez	Megara	Meg-ARE-a
	(The (E) is short as in	Nemean	Nem-EE-an
	'PET')	Augeas	OW-gee-ass
Cithaeron	SITH-air-on	Iolaus	Eye-OH-loss

Hera, queen of the gods and the wife of Zeus, was always the worst enemy of Herakles. Her hatred followed him all the days of his life.

When he was only a baby she sent two snakes to kill him in his cradle. Herakles, however, who was to be the greatest of the Greek heroes, was quite unafraid. He took each of the snakes by its neck and strangled it.

He became the strongest man in Greece and his adventures were talked about everywhere. He killed the Cithaeron lion. This was an animal that no one until then had been able to harm at all. Always after that he wore its skin which was tougher than the hardest armour. The lion's head rose up behind his own and the upper jaw with its sharp teeth came down like a cap.

Saving lives and helping people made him popular. Hera hated him all the more for that. Zeus had intended Herakles to rule in Argolis, a kingdom in Greece. But Hera managed it so that Eurystheus, his cousin reigned instead. And she sent Herakles even worse luck.

By this time Herakles was married and had children. His wife's name was Megara. One day Hera sent a fit of madness on Herakles. Mad and murderous, he did not know what he was doing. He thought his children were his enemies. In his rage and in spite of Megara's screams, he killed them all.

When he was sane again, he was heartbroken and accepted his punishment gladly. He had to submit to the cowardly king, Eurystheus, his cousin. Eurystheus was afraid of Herakles. He was glad to have the hero in his power but would rather have had him dead. He condemned Herakles to twelve seemingly impossible tasks.

Herakles had to kill the Nemean lion which was a task far greater than he had ever done before. He dealt with fearsome birds, a savage boar, a wild bull. He was ordered to capture a deer that belonged to a goddess and to bring back a belt that was owned by the queen of the Amazons. He had to steal cattle belonging to a giant and to tame man-eating horses. Eurystheus ordered him to clean the huge stables of Augeas, filthy with the muck of years. Herakles even brought back the golden apples of the Sun.

But his second task was almost the most difficult. He had to kill the Hydra. This was a monster that lived near a bottomless swamp. It had the body of a beast but it had nine necks. These writhed like the arms of an octopus and the nine heads had poisonous teeth. One of the heads was immortal and could not be killed at all. The very breath of the Hydra was poisonous. In fact, it was said that the scent left by the print of its feet could kill. Close to the swamp was a mountain and one of the entrances to Hell was supposed to be nearby. No one ever went near the place.

Herakles had a good friend, however, called Iolaus who was willing to drive him out there in his chariot. They stopped at the edge of the swamp to take a good look at what faced them.

Zeus, who felt sorry for his son, sent his messenger, the goddess Athena.

'The Hydra lives in a cave in the heart of the swamp,' she told Herakles. 'It would be certain death for you to go in after it. But you can drive it out into the open by shooting fire-arrows in there. Be careful not to breathe in its scent when you attack it. The smell of the Hydra can kill.'

Herakles thanked her and he and Iolaus went on into the swamp. When they came to the cave, Herakles did as Athena had advised. Iolaus lit a fire. Herakles tied dried grass to his arrows, lit it, and shot them into the cave.

With all its heads snarling and spitting, the Hydra charged out of its cave. But Herakles stood firm. Holding his breath, he chopped off the nearest head. Then he had to fall back in surprise and fear.

On the bleeding stump of the Hydra's neck two new heads had grown, each as savage as the one he had cut off. He had to give ground to draw breath and fight off the attacking Hydra as best he could. Each time he chopped off a head two new ones grew in its place. Herakles' strength was failing. With each wound it had, the Hydra grew stronger.

Hera saw what trouble he was in and sent a giant crab to grip his ankle with its claw and bring him down. Herakles, however, was still stronger than any other man and crushed the crab with his foot. But it almost looked as if the Hydra would beat him.

'Iolaus!' he gasped desperately. 'Build up the fire. Bind grass and twigs round a log and make a blazing torch.'

Iolaus asked no questions but worked as quickly as he could.

'The torch is well alight,' he told Herakles at last.

'Stand by me,' Herakles ordered. 'Have the torch ready. As I strike off each head, burn the neck with the torch.'

Fighting back his fear, Iolaus faced the monster at Herakles' side. The plan worked. The fire burnt the neck from which the head had gone. No fresh heads grew from the stump. When Herakles had the upper hand, it did not take him long to finish the fight.

The last head he cut off was the immortal head of the Hydra. As it lay on the ground, separated from the body, it growled and spat poison. Herakles dug a hole. Ignoring its attempts to bite him, he took it firmly by the neck and dropped it in. He filled the hole,

stamped the earth flat and put a great rock on top. It would have taken more than two men to move it again. The evil head was still hissing as the earth fell on it. No one has ever dared to dig it up. It may still lie there in wait to this day.

Herakles and his friend returned to Iolaus's chariot and drove back to the city. Herakles got no gratitude from Eurystheus for freeing the countryside from a savage monster. Eurystheus complained that Iolaus had helped Herakles. Herakles was supposed to do each of the tasks entirely alone.

Looking at the story again
1. How did Hera try to kill Herakles when he was a baby?
2. Why was it so hard to wound the Cithaeron lion?

3. What made Hera hate Herakles even more?
4. What was his punishment for killing his children?
5. Who helped him in his struggles with the Hydra?
6. Why did the Hydra at first grow stronger when Herakles cut its heads off?
7. How did they get rid of the immortal head of the Hydra?
8. What did Eurystheus complain about when Herakles returned?

Further questions
1. Herakles was famous because he had great strength. This was important in early times. What sort of gifts make a man important in our society?
2. What is a cradle?
3. What, in your opinion, was the worst thing Hera did to Herakles?
4. What was the most dangerous thing about the Hydra?
5. Why did Eurystheus want Herakles to be killed?
6. Could Herakles have defeated the Hydra without Iolaus? Give your views.

Things to do
1. Write a story in which a modern man digs up the head of the Hydra.
2. What sort of a man was Eurystheus? Describe his character and give reasons taken from the story for thinking as you do.
3. Make a list of the tasks that Herakles performed.
4. Look at the picture and draw one of your own for this story.
5. Describe the fight as if you were Iolaus.
6. Make a list of the five most dangerous jobs of the present day that you can think of. Write a story about one of them.
7. Write a poem called 'The Thing from the Cave' or 'The Unlucky One'.
8. The story can be divided up like this:
    (a) Hera sends madness on Herakles and he kills his children.
    (b) He is tried by a court and sentenced to serve Eurystheus.
    (c) Eurystheus tells him that he must kill the Hydra.
    (d) Herakles sets out with Iolaus and kills the monster.
    (e) He returns to Eurystheus.
   Act out all or part of the story.

Cerberus

Pronunciation Guide

Cerberus SIR-ber-us   Tantalus TAN-tal-us
Styx   Sticks   Sisyphus SISSY-fuss
Charon   CARE-on

The last task for Herakles was the hardest of all. It was almost too difficult even for a man whose father was a god.

Herakles had to go down into Hell and bring back the monstrous three-headed dog, Cerberus, that guarded the entrance there. Even finding his way down there was difficult. Wisely, Herakles asked for the help of the gods.

Athena showed him the way down into Hell. Hermes, messenger of the gods, went with him into the dark underworld.

The river Styx encircled Hell. There was a ferryman there called Charon. He rowed the souls of the dead across the Styx. He was not supposed to let any living man into Hell. Even the dead had to pay him a coin to be ferried across the river in his shadowy boat.

When Herakles scowled at him, however, Charon was too frightened to say a word. In silence he rowed Herakles and Hermes across the black river.

The first thing they saw on the other side was Medusa. Herakles made a move as if to defend them both but Hermes smiled and stopped him.

'You have forgotten,' Hermes said. 'They are ghosts down here. She cannot harm the gods or the living.'

They passed on through scenes of torment. One ghost, dying of thirst, stood tied to a pole in the middle of a pool of fresh water. Each time he bent down to drink, the level of the water dropped out of his reach. His name had been Tantalus. Another was forced to roll a heavy stone uphill. Whenever he was near the top, the stone slipped out of his hands and rolled all the way to the bottom again. His name had been Sisyphus.

At last they stood before the dark throne of Hades, king over all the dead. Herakles explained what he wanted.

'So you think you can master Cerberus?' said Hades. 'Well—you can try. But you must lay aside all weapons. Master him with your bare hands alone and you can take him.'

At the sight of Herakles, the three ugly heads of Cerberus growled together and three sets of fangs were bared. Herakles kicked out, as the dog came at him in a rush, and those fangs missed him by inches.

Then, in a flash the dog was at him again. Only the tough lion skin saved Herakles from the deadly bite of those poisonous teeth. Snarling, the dog tried to bite his throat. Herakles made a snatch and two of the dog's necks were in his iron fingers. The third head snarled and weaved about, trying to get at his face, but Herakles put forth all his strength and squeezed. Cerberus knew that he had met his match. In that grip his struggles rapidly weakened.

Hades was amazed. He was perhaps a little afraid, too. He had thought that nothing on Earth or in Hell could beat the power of Cerberus. But Hades kept his word. Charon rowed Hermes, Herakles and the savage monster back across the Styx and they made their way to the upper world and the sun.

As they came into the light, Cerberus made a last try to escape. Foam flew from his mouth as he writhed in the grip of Herakles. But his attempt failed. Herakles had him fast. Where the foam had fallen on the ground, poisonous flowers sprang up.

Herakles at last entered the hall of Eurystheus. Hermes, seeing him successful, had left him. When Eurystheus saw the terrible beast, he screamed.

'I have done what you asked,' said Herakles. 'Do you want to keep the dog? Shall I let it go?'

'No! No!' pleaded Eurystheus. 'Hold it fast!'

'I have done everything you ordered,' said Herakles. 'It has taken eight years. Is my punishment over?'

'Yes,' cried Eurystheus. 'You are free. I no longer have any power over you. Your tasks are finished. Go. But take that evil monster with you.'

Herakles smiled grimly. He left the hall and went back to the underworld. He returned the three-headed dog to its master, Hades. No one would ever again dare to tackle Cerberus. Only Herakles could master the watch-dog of Hell.

Looking at the story again

1. What was the most unusual thing about Cerberus?
2. Who went with Herakles into the underworld?
3. What was Charon's job?
4. Whom did they meet first on the other side of the river?

5. What was the punishment of Sisyphus?
6. What protected Herakles from the bites of Cerberus?
7. What grew from the foam that fell from the dog's mouth?
8. What did Eurystheus do when he saw Cerberus?
9. What happened to Cerberus in the end?

Further questions
1. Why was it necessary for Hermes to go with Herakles? What help did he give Herakles?
2. Which ghost, Tantalus or Sisyphus, had the worst punishment? Explain why you think so.
3. In what ways is this Greek idea of the Underworld different from the Christian idea of Hell?
4. Name as many poisonous flowers and berries as you can.
5. Had Eurystheus expected Herakles to bring Cerberus? What had he been hoping for? Explain how you know.
6. Why did Herakles return Cerberus to Hades? Why did he not kill the dog?

Things to do
1. Look at the picture and draw one of your own for this story.
2. Find out why Tantalus and Sisyphus had earned their punishment and write down what each of them had done.
3. Write a poem called 'Underground River' or 'Journey in the Dark'.
4. Another living man, Orpheus, is supposed to have visited the Greek Underworld. Find out about his story and re-tell it.
5. Write about the most difficult job you have ever done.
6. Write out Charon's part of the story as if you were Charon himself.
7. The story can be divided up like this:
    (a) Eurystheus orders Herakles to bring him Cerberus.
    (b) Herakles asks the help of the gods.
    (c) The trip down to and through the underworld.
    (d) The meeting with Hades.
    (e) The capture of Cerberus and the return to the real world.
    (f) The meeting with Eurystheus.
  Act out part or all of the story.

The Chimera

It has been said that all the Greek myths link up into one long story. In this story about Bellerophon, there are certainly links with other myths. Sisyphus, whom Herakles met in Hades, was the grandfather of Bellerophon. Pegasus, the winged horse, was born from the blood of Medusa when Perseus beheaded her.

Pronunciation Guide

Bellerophon	Bell-ERR-off-on (The ERR is the same sound as the start of the word 'error')	Lycia	LISS-i-a
		Chimera	KIM-er-a
		Polybius	Poll-IBB-i-us
		Pegasus	PEG-ass-us
		Amazons	AM-ah-zuns
Iobates	Eye-oh-BART-eez	Solymnians	Sol-IMM-ny-anz

Someone had been telling lies about Bellerophon. Iobates, king of Lycia, believed them. Bellerophon's enemies said that he was an evil young man who deserved death. Iobates ordered Bellerophon to kill the Chimera. This was a monster with a lion's head, the body of a goat and a dragon's tail. Many men before had tried to kill it. They had all died, burned to ashes in the Chimera's fiery breath. Bellerophon, knowing that he faced certain death, went to see his friend, Polybius.

'A mere man can't help you out of danger like that,' the wise old man told him. 'Go to the temple of Athena and pray to the goddess for help.'

It was a slight ray of hope. Bellerophon travelled to the temple and then after his prayers, as night was coming on, he lay down to sleep. He dreamed that Athena appeared to him. She told him of a winged horse called Pegasus. Each day at dawn the splendid animal would come to a spring near the temple and drink. Athena showed Bellerophon a golden bridle. Any man who threw it over the horse's neck would be able to capture it and ride it. Mounted on Pegasus, Bellerophon could fly down on the Chimera. That way he would have a chance of ridding the country of the monster and escaping alive.

To his surprise, Bellerophon woke with the bridle in his hand. He found the spring Athena had spoken of and waited for the sun to rise. As the first rays of light came into the sky, the horse glided down like a swan and drank. It was not hard for Bellerophon to bridle it and to climb on its back. It made no protest when he urged it on. Its strong wings carried them up into the brightening sky.

It was easy, too, to find the Chimera. Mounted on Pegasus, Bellerophon could see the countryside spread out below him. The patches of scorched grass and the burned trees marked the track of the monster. Bellerophon followed the signs until he saw the Chimera. It was prowling a stretch of open country. It did not know that it was being watched.

Bellerophon flew back to the city and put Pegasus in a safe hiding place. He armed himself with a bow and arrows and a good sword. On his back he carried a bag in which was a lump of lead. He had worked out a plan of attack and hoped it would succeed.

Pegasus carried him and the extra weight easily enough and it was not long before they came upon the Chimera again. Bellerophon swooped on it, firing his arrows. Though his aim was good, they had little effect on the tough skin of the monster. It had seen its attacker and was ready. As Bellerophon dived on it a second time, striking out with his sword, the Chimera reared up, slashing at him with its claws. But Pegasus was too quick for it. Bellerophon repeated his attacks. But although the speed of his horse saved him from real harm, he found that he could only slightly wound the monster with his sword. He flew up to be out of danger and in a safe place high in the air he unstrapped the bag on his back. What he was going to do was dangerous but it seemed his best chance of finishing the monster.

Once more he dived to the attack. The Chimera watched him come, lashing its tail and roaring. Flames crackled from its gaping mouth. Pegasus was circling. The monster turned this way and that, trying to decide from which direction Bellerophon and the flying horse would come. Then, suddenly, Bellerophon was on top of it.

The Chimera reared to meet them. For a second they flew through the searing flames of its breath. But then they were past and Bellerophon had pushed the lump of metal deep into those yawning jaws.

The monster choked, shaking its head desperately. But the lead was jammed hard down its throat. The soft metal melted in the fierce heat of its breath. As the drops of liquid metal ate into its body, it roared with pain. From a height, Bellerophon watched the creature lash about in its death agonies and finally lie still.

He took the good news back to Iobates. But Iobates still did not trust him. Twice more he tested the young man's bravery. First he sent him out against the Amazons who were attacking Lycia. Then Bellerophon had to drive off a tribe called the Solymnians. Bellerophon beat off both attacks with the help of Pegasus. He flew above their armies and dropped rocks on them. Both the Amazons and the Solymnians fled in terror.

At last Iobates realised that Bellerophon was no criminal but a hero. He changed completely towards the young man and let Bellerophon marry his daughter. For some years after that Bellerophon and his family lived happily enough in Lycia.

As Bellerophon grew older, however, he became proud and foolish. He decided that he would visit the gods in Olympus as if he were one of them. On Pegasus he flew higher and higher until he was almost in sight of the Olympian heaven. Zeus, father of all the gods, punished him for his pride. He sent a gadfly to sting Pegasus. Pegasus reared at the pain, throwing Bellerophon from his back. Bellerophon ended his days sadly. Though not killed by the fall through the favour of the gods, he wandered Greece as an outcast and a cripple.

Men say that Zeus was kinder to the white winged horse. He made him immortal and set him as a sign in heaven. You can see to this day in the winter sky a group of stars called Pegasus.

Looking at the story again
1. What did Bellerophon's enemies say about him?
2. What had happened to the other men who had tried to kill the Chimera?
3. How did Bellerophon capture the winged horse?
4. What signs marked the track of the Chimera?

5. Why could Bellerophon not wound the Chimera with his arrows?
6. How did Bellerophon kill the monster?
7. How did he drive away the armies that were attacking Lycia?
8. What did Bellerophon decide to do when he grew older?
9. How did he end his days?
10. What happened to Pegasus?

Further questions

1. What was there about Pegasus which would help in the fight against the Chimera?
2. Why could the Chimera not see Bellerophon when he first watched it?
3. How do you know Pegasus could move very quickly in the air?
4. Explain how the lead killed the monster.
5. What made Iobates at last trust Bellerophon?
6. How do you know that Zeus was not angry with Pegasus?

Things to do

1. You fly over your own town on Pegasus. Describe some of the things you would see. You can draw a map or write about them.
2. Write about any dream of flying you have had.
3. Write a poem called 'Wings' or 'Stargazing'.
4. How many groups of stars can you recognise? Draw a map and name each group.
5. Phaëthon also flew across the sky. Find out what happened to him and write the story.
6. Write Bellerophon's story as if you were Bellerophon himself near the end of his life.
7. Look at the picture and draw one of your own for the story.
8. This tale can be divided up like this:
   (a) Iobates orders Bellerophon to kill the Chimera.
   (b) Athena comes to Bellerophon in a dream.
   (c) Bellerophon's attack on the Chimera.
   (d) Bellerophon attacks the Amazons and Solymnians.
   (e) Bellerophon tries to fly to heaven.
   Act out all or part of the story.

The Cyclops

Odysseus was away from home so long that many people thought he was dead. Some of them tried to take over his kingdom from his wife. When Odysseus did return he was strong enough and brave enough to defeat his enemies almost single-handed. But he was a hero to the Greeks mainly because of his cleverness in a tight corner.

You probably remember how the Greeks captured Troy. They used a large wooden horse in which many men could hide. Leaving the horse, they pretended to sail away. The Trojans then dragged the horse inside their city. After dark, the Greeks hidden inside the horse came out and opened the gates of the city for their friends. The city of Troy was captured.

It was Odysseus who had thought of that rather crafty plan. Here is another example of his quick thinking. It is an incident on his long journey home after the Trojan War.

Pronunciation Guide

Odysseus	o-DISS-ee-us	Polyphemus	Polly-FEEM-us
Ithaca	ITH-ah-ka	Poseidon	Poss-EYE-don
Cyclops	SIGH-klops		

The Greeks had won the war in Troy. Now Odysseus and his men could sail home to Ithaca in Greece. But they would not have an easy voyage. They had killed and eaten some of the cattle of the gods and the gods were angry. Odysseus and his crew were already a long way off their course. Food was short.

When they saw an island they decided to land and explore. They could see many flocks of sheep and goats. Odysseus chose a small party of men and went inland. He took with him a large skin bag full of good strong wine. It would be a suitable present for whoever ruled on the island.

Soon they came to a cave. It was very large inside with a high roof.

In it they found great bowls of goat's milk and cheese. Lambs were also penned up inside. But there was no sign of a human owner. Some of the men wanted to take what they could and go quickly back to the ships. But Odysseus decided to wait for the owner of the flocks. They were warriors and not thieves.

When the owner appeared, they were filled with alarm. He was one of the tribe of Cyclops, giants with a single eye in their forehead. He was as tall as the tallest tree and his name was Polyphemus. He followed his flock of sheep and goats into the cave and he had blocked the entrance with a boulder the size of a house before he saw Odysseus and his frightened crew.

'Who are you?' he growled in a voice like thunder. 'Pirates? Or traders?'

'We are warriors, returning from the war in Troy,' Odysseus told him. 'We have been blown off our course.'

Polyphemus, the Cyclops, only grunted. He did not speak again until he had milked his goats. He poured the milk into his enormous bowls and let the lambs feed. Odysseus grew impatient.

'Show us kindness and hospitality,' he suggested, 'and the gods will reward you.'

'The gods?' roared Polyphemus. He had finished his tasks and turned savagely on Odysseus. 'I do not fear the gods. I have no need of the gods. What are they to me? Where's your ship?'

'It was wrecked,' Odysseus told him craftily, fearing danger.

'Wrecked, eh?' Polyphemus growled. He was crouching down but he still towered over them. 'Good,' he said, staring at their tense faces. He licked his lips. Suddenly he reached out, grabbed two of the men, one in each hand and smashed their heads against the cave wall. Then, snorting and grunting, he ate them, crunching their bones. When he had finished, he wiped his mouth with his hand, lay down and slept.

Seeing the death of their comrades, the men had cried aloud. Now they were silent and terrified. Odysseus's sword was in his hand ready to kill the giant. Then he looked at the great rock which blocked the entrance. He and all his men would never move it. If he killed the Cyclops, they would be prisoners until they died.

Few of them slept for long that night. When dawn came, Polyphemus woke, snatched two more of the terrified men and ate them. Then he looked after his flocks and drove them out of the cave to feed. He took care to see that no one could escape and blocked the entrance with the boulder as he left.

During the long night, however, Odysseus had thought of a plan. In the cave tree trunks were lying about. The giant used them as sticks to help him to walk over the rough hills and to drive his flocks. Odysseus cut six feet off the end of one of these and ordered his men to light a fire. With their swords they sharpened the end of the staff and hardened its point by burning it in the flames.

Evening came and the giant returned, driving his flocks into the cave and closing the entrance with the block of stone. He milked his goats before he took two more men and ate them with horrible relish.

Before he went to sleep, Odysseus, disguising his feelings, offered him a bowl of wine.

'Here,' he said. 'I brought this wine hoping to find kindly people on this island. Take it and drink. If you treat visitors in this way, you'll get no more gifts.'

The Cyclops drank and was pleased. 'Give me some more,' he ordered, holding out the bowl. Odysseus poured it full again. The Cyclops drank three huge bowls of the wine.

'This is good stuff,' he said, smacking his lips. 'What's your name?'

'My name?' said crafty Odysseus. 'I am called—Nobody.'

'Nobody, eh?' The Cyclops was quite drunk. 'Well, Nobody, this is splendid wine. You'll get a reward for this. I'll eat you last of all.' He began to mumble then and shortly afterwards fell on his back in a deep, drunken sleep.

Odysseus and his men got the fire going well. They took the stake which they had hidden and put it in the flames. When it was just about to burn, they took it out and drove it into the single eye of the Cyclops.

He gave a great scream of pain and threw himself about the cave, howling and yelling. Odysseus and his men ran and dodged as his huge hands groped to crush them. But he did not catch them.

All the other giants who lived on the island were awakened by the noise. They came to the entrance to the cave.

'Polyphemus!' they shouted. 'What is wrong? Is someone attacking you?'

'Nobody!' he yelled. 'Nobody is attacking me!' Between rage and pain he could hardly speak. The other giants thought he must have been dreaming and went back to their caves to sleep.

When he had partly recovered, Polyphemus rolled away the stone from the mouth of the cave. He sat there with his arms spread to catch anyone who might try to escape.

But Odysseus's plan was thorough. He picked out the biggest animals in Polyphemus's flock and tied them together, side by side, in threes. Each of his men would cling to the middle animal as he hung underneath it. The ones on each side of him would hide and protect him.

At dawn, the animals, knowing that it was time to go out, moved towards the entrance. As each group of three passed him, the giant felt along their sides and over their backs. He wanted to make sure that they were not carrying any men. But he could not feel underneath the middle animal where each of Odysseus's companions was hanging.

Odysseus left the cave last. He was slung underneath the largest ram in the flock. It was a terrifying moment. The giant recognised the ram and held it back.

'Usually you are out of the cave first,' he said. 'You lead the flock. Why are you last of all this morning?' But his fumbling hands did not find Odysseus.

Free, Odysseus and his men hurried down to the shore. They wasted few words in telling the rest of the crew what had happened. Swiftly they bent to their oars and rowed away. But Polyphemus had got what he deserved and Odysseus wanted to tell him so.

'Cyclops!' he shouted. 'You have treated strangers cruelly. You have murdered, you have eaten human flesh, you have spoken scornfully of the gods. My name is not Nobody but Odysseus. I, Odysseus, tell you that you have received just punishment.'

He spoke too soon. Polyphemus stood on the cliff top. With a roar of rage he lifted an enormous rock and flung it into the sea. It crashed in front of Odysseus's ship. The wave it made washed them back nearly on to the land.

Odysseus would have shouted more insults to Polyphemus but his men asked him to be quiet. They watched the giant as he stood on the cliff. Polyphemus lifted his arms to heaven and called on Poseidon, the god of the sea. He prayed for revenge on Odysseus and his crew.

Poseidon heard his prayer. The voyage home was even longer and more unlucky than it might have been. Only Odysseus reached home alive in the end and he suffered many hardships.

Looking at the story again

1. Why were Odysseus and his men returning home?
2. What present did Odysseus take on to the island?
3. Why did Odysseus decide to wait in the cave until the owner returned?
4. With what did Polyphemus block the mouth of the cave?
5. Why did Odysseus not kill Polyphemus with his sword?
6. What happened when dawn came?
7. How was Polyphemus going to reward Odysseus for the wine?
8. Why did Polyphemus not find Odysseus and his men as they escaped from the cave?
9. What did Polyphemus do when Odysseus called out to him as the ship was leaving?
10. To whom did Polyphemus pray and what did he pray for?

Further questions

1. What was the reason for Odysseus and his men landing on the island?
2. Describe the appearance of Polyphemus.
3. Why was Polyphemus glad to hear that Odysseus had been wrecked?
4. Why did Odysseus give Polyphemus the wine to drink?
5. Why did Odysseus not tell Polyphemus his real name?
6. Do you think Odysseus was fair in the punishment he gave Polyphemus? Give your reasons.

Things to do

1. What are the advantages of being a giant? Make a list. Can you think of any disadvantages?
2. Write a poem called 'One-Eyed Monster' or 'The Drunken Giant'.

3. Look at the picture and draw one of your own for this story.
4. The home of Odysseus was in Ithaca. Find out where that is and where Troy used to be and draw a map of the Eastern Mediterranean, putting in both places and any others that seem to you of interest.
5. Write the story as if you were Polyphemus.
6. What was your favourite story about a giant when you were a child? Write it out as if for a five-year-old.
7. How many other words can you think of beside 'enormous' which mean 'of great size'?
8. The story can be divided up like this:
    (a) Odysseus and his men land.
    (b) They decide to explore and find the cave.
    (c) They argue about whether to leave or not and are found by the giant.
    (d) The men are eaten, they make a plan and the giant is blinded.
    (e) They escape from the cave.
    (f) Odysseus taunts Polyphemus when they are back on board their ship.

Act out all or part of the story.

Grendel

These tales from Northern Europe are later in time than those of the Greeks. The gods do not play so large a part in them. The monsters are more like human beings and less like animals.

As you can see, the great virtue for these people was loyalty, the responding to the claims of friendship. Beowulf obviously feels that such things are important.

Eventually, Beowulf became king over his own people. The long poem about him does not tell whether he ever visited Hrothgar again. It does, however, tell of his death. Helped by one young warrior, he fought and killed a dragon, dying himself in the attempt. Though old and no longer the man he had been, he gave his life in defence of his kingdom and his people.

Pronunciation Guide

Hrothgar	H-ROTH-gar	Unferth	UN-firth
Grendel	GREN-dle	Breca	BRECK-a
Beowulf	BAY-oh-wolf	Wealtheow	WALE-thee-ow

Hrothgar, the king, built a great hall in Denmark. But he got little pleasure from it. At first bright fires burned there; men feasted and drank and sang.

But they were watched with eyes of envy. Grendel, the monster, the man-eater, spied on the merry-making.

One night, while a group of Hrothgar's warriors slept, Grendel came to the hall. Over the misty moors he came like a dark shadow. There were thirty men in the hall that night. Grendel killed them all and carried off their bodies.

Next day Hrothgar and his warriors were silent with horror as they saw the empty hall. There were pools of blood. Huge, bloody footprints marked where Grendel had been. And he came again the next night. They left the hall to the monster after that. No man would sleep there. Grendel roamed at night. He killed and ate as he wished. No man and no group of men dared face him.

Beowulf heard the news. His father was an old friend of Hrothgar's. Beowulf took fourteen men and sailed out from Sweden. As they neared Denmark, the watchman on the coast saw them coming. When they came ashore, he asked what they wanted. Beowulf told him why they had come and they were taken to Hrothgar.

'Beowulf!' said Hrothgar. 'I knew your father well.'

'I have heard of your trouble,' Beowulf told him. 'Let me and my men sleep in your hall tonight.'

'Grendel is a monster,' Hrothgar warned. 'He is stronger than any man and a man-eater, too.'

'A man-eater?' said Beowulf. 'Then, if I fail, my burial will not be expensive. But never fear. I have faced monsters before. Can we sleep in your hall?'

Hrothgar could not refuse. He was glad of Beowulf's help. First, however, he gave Beowulf and his men a great feast. There was plenty to drink. Unferth was one of Hrothgar's men. He had been looking enviously at Beowulf. Suddenly he spoke.

'Aren't you the Beowulf who had a bet with Breca?' he asked. 'You said you would both spend many days at sea. The one who was the best hunter would win the bet. Breca won. You lost.'

'You've drunk too much beer, Unferth,' Beowulf told him. 'I had a bet with Breca. He is a good friend of mine. We were five days at sea. It was winter; the waves were rough and the winds ice-cold. We were separated. A sea-beast attacked my boat and turned it over. I fought it beneath the waves with my sword. Others attacked me. I fought with them all. In the morning I was on a snowy beach. There were nine dead sea-beasts round me. It was more than Breca did. And more than you have ever done, Unferth. You talk too much. When you've killed a monster like Grendel, you might be worth listening to.'

The warriors laughed. Unferth's eyes were red with drink and anger but he did not speak again.

Wealtheow, the queen, welcomed Beowulf and wished him well. Beowulf repeated his vow. He would rid the land of Grendel or die. No one laughed at that.

The feasting ended and the warriors of Hrothgar left the hall with their king and queen. Beowulf and his men lay down to sleep there. Beowulf put away his sword and his armour. He would meet Grendel man to man and hand to hand. It was part of his vow.

Grendel came over the misty moors, eager to taste human flesh. The door had iron bolts to hold it. Grendel tore them open and was in among the sleeping men. His eyes shone in the dark like blue flames.

He seized one of the men and bit into him, drinking his blood. In no time he had eaten him whole, even his feet and hands. Grendel reached out for Beowulf.

Then he knew that he had never felt a grip like this before. Beowulf held the monster fast. Grendel was afraid. He knew he had met his match and fought to get out of the hall. But Beowulf held on to him. The monster threw him this way and that but Beowulf's grip did not weaken. The hall boomed to the sound of the fight as the two crashed against walls and benches. Beowulf's men were up with their swords in their hands. But swords had no effect on Grendel's tough hide.

Grendel screamed in pain and terror. His shoulder was cracking. He gave a mighty wrench. He was free. But he was wounded to death. He had torn his arm out of its shoulder. It was left in Beowulf's grip. The wounded monster staggered out of the hall and made his escape. Some followed but did not challenge him. He ran across the moors and dived into a black lake. The water seemed to boil. Blood was on the waves. He did not come up again.

Many came to see the mighty arm. Beowulf had nailed it above the door of the hall. It was huge, scaly and grey. The claws on the hand were like spikes of steel. Hrothgar came and praised Beowulf.

Another feast was held. Hrothgar gave Beowulf many presents. Beowulf received a golden banner, armour, a helmet and a sword. He was given eight horses. Each of his companions was given a sword, too, and Hrothgar paid much gold for the companion of Beowulf whom Grendel had killed.

Then the hall was cleaned and made ready and the feast was held. Wealtheow, the queen, gave Beowulf more presents. He had a golden collar from her, arm rings and shirt of armour.

Then the fires burned again in Hrothgar's hall. There was feasting and singing and telling of tales as there had been before Grendel came. When the night was old, men slept in Hrothgar's hall once more. Grendel was dead.

No one there knew then of the sea witch, Grendel's mother.

Looking at the story again

1. In what country was Hrothgar's hall?
2. How many men did Grendel kill on his first visit?
3. From what country did Beowulf sail?
4. Who first saw Beowulf's ship?
5. How many sea-beasts did Beowulf kill?
6. Why could Beowulf's men not kill Grendel with their swords?
7. What did Grendel do after he escaped from Beowulf?
8. What did Grendel's arm look like?
9. What presents did Wealtheow give Beowulf?

Further questions

1. Why did Hrothgar get little pleasure from his great hall?
2. What fuel would be used on the fires there?
3. What reasons might Beowulf have for helping Hrothgar?
4. How did Hrothgar feel about accepting Beowulf's help?
5. Why was Unferth envious of Beowulf?
6. Why did Beowulf want to meet Grendel without weapons or armour?
7. Why could Beowulf not save one of his men from Grendel?
8. Name some of the things that people in those days used instead of money.
9. Give one word which describes a man who eats human flesh.
10. How many other words can you think of that means 'warrior'?

Things to do

1. Write a description of Beowulf or Grendel.
2. Draw a sketch map of Denmark and Sweden. Name the sea between them. Put in Beowulf's voyage between the two countries.
3. 'Over the *m*isty *m*oors grim *G*rendel came,
   *S*tealthy was his *s*talking to the *s*ilent hall . . .'

Write a poem about some strange animal or happening in which many of the words begin with the same letter.

4. Write a description of Beowulf's voyage and the events in the hall as if you were one of his men.

5. Find some pictures of Anglo-Saxon jewellery and draw some of the gifts that Beowulf received.

6. Look at the picture and draw one of your own for this story.

7. With the help of your library, draw a plan of Hrothgar's hall or a sketch of Beowulf's ship.

8. As if it had happened to you, write a story about a swimmer's fight with some sea creatures.

9. Write a poem called 'The Longships' or 'The Deep, Dark Lake' or 'The Man Eater'.

10. The story divides into several parts:

   (a) Hrothgar's men see what Grendel has done.

   (b) Beowulf hears the news.

   (c) Beowulf and his men arrive in Denmark.

   (d) Beowulf talks to Hrothgar and Unferth is envious.

   (e) Grendel attacks the hall and is driven off.

   (f) There is a feast to celebrate Grendel's defeat.

Act out all or part of the story.

The Sea Witch

Pronunciation Guide
Aeschere   ASH-air
Hrunting   H-RUNT-ing

The sea witch came in the very early morning to avenge her dead son, Grendel. The men who had been sleeping in Hrothgar's hall grabbed their spears and shields. But she was too quick for them. She vanished like a shadow into the darkness. And she took with her Aeschere, the best of Hrothgar's men, and the arm of her son, Grendel.

Beowulf had not been sleeping in the hall that night. When he heard the news, he hurried to Hrothgar.

'Men talked of two monsters. That was hard to believe,' Hrothgar said. 'But now we know. She has taken Aeschere, the best of men and my friend. It is said that she lives far from here in an evil place. To reach it one must go by cliff paths and across the moors where wolves roam. Her home is in a dark pool at the edge of the moor. You have helped us once, Beowulf. Will you help us again?'

'Do not grieve for your dead friend, Hrothgar,' Beowulf told him. 'It is better to think of revenge than sorrow. If it is my fate, I shall kill this sea witch for you. Let us go.'

Beowulf and his companions went with Hrothgar and his men. Along forest tracks they went and up into the hills until they reached the cliffs. There, they climbed narrow, dangerous paths until they came to the moors. Beyond these was a dark wood. Its trees surrounded a black pool. In the reeds by the pool they found Aeschere's head. They stood in silence looking at it in horror and sadness.

There was blood on the surface of the pool and around it lay strange monsters. One of Beowulf's men blew his battle horn and another fired an arrow. At the sound of the horn, the monsters dived into the water but one lay dead, pierced by the arrow. They dragged it on to the land, looking at its ugliness in wonder and disgust.

Beowulf put on his armour and his helmet. Unferth stepped forward. Now he had only admiration for Beowulf.

'Take my sword,' he offered. 'It is called Hrunting. It is the best of weapons and with its help I have won many battles.'

Beowulf thanked him and took the sword. Then he dived into the dark, cold water. It was a long way down. The monsters attacked him. But his armour kept him safe and he drove them off with the good sword, Hrunting.

In the depths, the sea witch was waiting. She seized him in her terrible claws. Again his armour saved him from wounds. But she dragged him into her cave.

It lay above the water line and he could breathe air again. There was even enough light in the cave to see by. He freed his arm from her grip and swung his sword. Again and again he struck. But its edge had no power against her iron skin. She was like her son, Grendel, and swords made by men could not harm her.

Beowulf threw the sword aside and seized her with his hands. The sea witch had a dagger but his armour resisted her strokes. Their wrestling was long and fierce. She was stronger than Grendel had been. The fight went on and on.

As Beowulf weakened, he realised that he could not win with only his bare hands. He looked round the cave. Many weapons hung on its walls. One sword was huge. It had been made by dwarfs for a giant when the world was young. No ordinary man could have lifted it.

Putting out all his strength, Beowulf broke free from the witch. He ran to the wall and tore the giant's sword from its fastening. Two-handed, he swung it as the sea witch rushed at him. It cut through flesh and bone. Headless and without even a scream she fell to the floor. Her blood ran away into the water.

Near the water's edge, the dead body of Grendel was lying. Beowulf thought of all the harm Grendel had done. He raised the sword and cut off the monster's head. Again the water was stained with blood.

Up above by the pool Hrothgar and his men were waiting. Suddenly one of them cried out. He pointed to the redness that was coming to the surface. Hrothgar hid his face in his hands. When he lifted his head once more, he spoke sorrowfully.

'Let us go,' he said. 'Beowulf is dead. The hero has fought his last battle.' Sadly he left with all his men. Beowulf's companions stayed. But their eyes, fixed on the pool, were hopeless, too.

In the cave Beowulf stared at the blade of the giant's sword. Grendel's poisonous blood worked on it like acid. The thick metal blade was disappearing like an icicle held in front of a hot fire. In a moment only the hilt was left in his hand.

He picked up the sword, Hrunting, and put it in his belt. Then he twisted his fingers in Grendel's hair and with the hilt of the giant's sword in one hand and the head in the other he swam to the surface.

His men gave a great shout when they saw him. Eager hands reached for him to pull him out of the water. With Grendel's head carried on a spear, Beowulf and his companions went back to Hrothgar's hall.

Hrothgar was delighted to see him safe. Men crowded round to see the evil head of the monster.

'The sea witch and her son are both dead,' Beowulf told Hrothgar. 'Neither of them will ever bother you and your people again.' He told Hrothgar what had happened in the cave. He described the way in which the sea witch had died and what had happened when he cut off Grendel's head.

'Here is the hilt of that great sword.' He showed it to Hrothgar. 'This is all that is left of it. But it has many beautiful carvings on it. Keep it, Hrothgar. Take it as a present from me. It will tell you that the evil days have gone whenever you look at it.'

Peace had come to Hrothgar's hall and there was a great feast that night. Beowulf and Hrothgar swore undying friendship.

'If danger ever threatens you and your people,' Beowulf promised, 'send word to me and I will come.'

Hrothgar thanked him again. Beowulf slept well that night after his long battle.

In the morning Beowulf and his men went to their ship. They carried with them all the treasure they had received at Hrothgar's court. At last they hoisted the sails and set out for the open sea. With his people Hrothgar watched, sad-faced. He was old. He might not see Beowulf again.

Looking at the story again

1. What did the sea witch take away with her from Hrothgar's hall?
2. Where was her home?
3. What did Hrothgar and his men find in the reeds by the pool?
4. Who gave Beowulf a special sword?
5. How could Beowulf breathe in the sea witch's cave?
6. Why did the sword, Hrunting, not harm the sea witch?
7. What did Beowulf find on the wall of the cave to help him?
8. Why did Hrothgar and his men leave the pool?
9. What final present did Beowulf give Hrothgar?
10. Why was Hrothgar sad when Beowulf left his court?

Further questions

1. Why did one of Beowulf's men blow the battle horn and another fire the arrow?
2. Why was it surprising that Unferth should give Beowulf his sword?
3. How might the sea witch have known that Beowulf was swimming down through the water to attack her?
4. Why was it only the giant's sword that could kill the sea witch?
5. Why did Beowulf cut off Grendel's head?

Things to do

1. You are a skin diver, swimming far out in a bay, who finds a ship. Describe your underwater journey.
2. Look at the pictures and draw one of your own for this story.
3. Write a poem called 'The Wood of Mystery' or 'The Battle Horn'.
4. Find out about and make a list of great swimming feats, putting them in what you think are their order of importance.
5. What happened when Beowulf got home? Describe his voyage into harbour and the later conversations on shore.
6. Using the information from the story, draw a map of Beowulf's journey from Hrothgar's hall to the witch's lair. The map can be illustrated with small pictures.
7. Tell the story as if you were Unferth. Remember that he changed his mind about Beowulf.

8. The story can be divided up as follows:
   (a) The sea witch attacks and carries off Aeschere.
   (b) Beowulf and his companions go to the dark pool.
   (c) The monsters are driven off and Beowulf is given Hrunting.
   (d) Beowulf fights the sea witch in the cave.
   (e) Hrothgar decides that Beowulf is dead and leaves.
   (f) Beowulf's return is greeted by his men.
   (g) Beowulf talks to Hrothgar before leaving his court.

   Act out all or part of the story.

Fafnir

This tale of a hero and a dragon is part of a much longer story. In it the hero wins a magic cap which can change his appearance. He frees a beautiful girl from a magical circle of fire. In the German version, the hero is called Siegfried. The full story of all his adventures is the subject of a series of operas by the German composer, Richard Wagner.

Pronunciation Guide

Fafnir	FAFF-near	Sigmund	SEEG-mund
Siegfried	SEEG-freed	Gram	Grarm
Wagner	VARG-ner	Regin	REGG-in
Andvari	And-VARR-i	Odin	OWE-din
Hreidmar	H-RIDE-mar	Grane	GRAR-ner
Sigurd	SEE-goord		

A great treasure had been stolen, first from Andvari and then from Hreidmar, who were two dwarf-kings. Both of them had put a powerful curse on it. Fafnir had killed his father, Hreidmar, for the gold. Magic and the curse on the treasure had turned him into a dragon. Huge, scaly and evil he lived alone in the wilderness, guarding the treasure and nursing his hatred of all men.

Sigurd's father, Sigmund, had been a great hero but had died in battle before Sigurd was born. In that battle Sigmund's mighty sword, Gram, had been broken into pieces. Sigurd had been brought up by the dwarf, Regin. Regin was a smith. He treated the young lad badly and made him work hard. There was no kindness in Regin's heart for Sigurd. But he let the boy live. Regin schemed to get the treasure and his mind was evil.

In spite of all Regin's ill-treatment, Sigurd grew to be a man, strong, fearless and honest. Regin thought the time was ripe. He told Sigurd of the treasure, describing its beauty.

'What do I need with treasure?' Sigurd asked. 'I am young and no weakling. I can make my own way in the world without gold to begin with.'

'You will need a sword to do that,' Regin said. There was a sly look in his eye. 'I will make you the best sword you have ever seen if you will promise to get the treasure.'

'That would be a fine thing to have,' said Sigurd. 'Make it and I will try to kill Fafnir for you.'

Regin took some of the best iron. He blew up his fire and hammered out a great sword on his anvil. When, at last, it was finished, he showed it to Sigurd. 'Try it,' he said.

Eagerly Sigurd swung it over his head and brought it down on a block of wood. But his strength was so great that the blow shattered the sword. Regin's face was dark with anger and disappointment. He sent Sigurd to fetch the broken pieces of his father's sword, Gram. Regin had to work hard to repair that sword. It was difficult work and many days passed. But, finally, the sword, Gram, was made new again. Regin gave it to Sigurd. 'Strike a blow with that,' he ordered.

Sigurd's eyes were bright with pleasure. He swung the sword and brought it down, this time on the anvil. It cut the anvil in half. Its edge was still sharp enough to cut a strand of wool drifting in the air.

'You have Gram, the finest sword in the world,' Regin said. 'Keep your promise. Kill Fafnir. When he is dead, bring me the dragon's heart and his treasure.'

Sigurd set out for the wilderness. When he came near the dragon's cave he met an old man, dressed in grey, with only one eye. This was Odin, father of all the Northern gods, in human form. Sigurd did not know who the old man was but he took his advice all the same.

The dragon's back and sides were covered with scales that no sword could pierce. Only a wound in its underside would have a chance of killing it. Odin told Sigurd to dig a pit outside the cave and hide in it. He should dig it so that it lay in the path of the dragon when Fafnir entered or left his cave. As the writhing body of the dragon passed over him, Sigurd should strike upwards with his sword.

While Fafnir was sleeping, Sigurd dug a pit and hid himself there. When the dragon woke, he sensed that a human being was near. Roaring and spitting flame and poison, he came out of the cave. Sigurd drove his sword into the monster up to the hilt.

Even dying, the dragon was still terrible. He tore the earth, uprooted trees and cracked rocks as he clawed at them in his death agony. As he lay helpless and weak at last, he saw Sigurd.

'What is the name of the man who has killed me?' asked Fafnir.

'My name is Sigurd, son of Sigmund,' Sigurd told him.

'The gold you take from my cave will be a curse to you,' Fafnir told him. 'And there is a dwarf. His name is Regin. I leave you to him.' And Fafnir lay still.

Seeing the dragon safely dead, Sigurd did as Regin had ordered. He cut out its heart. As he did so, a drop of Fafnir's blood fell on his lips and the world was changed. He could understand the language of birds.

'Why does Sigurd take the dragon's heart to Regin?' one bird asked.

'Sigurd should eat it himself. It will give him some of Fafnir's power,' said another.

'Fafnir was a dragon but Regin is worse,' said a third. 'There is more cunning and danger in Regin than there was in Fafnir.'

'Sigurd will have no chance to eat the dragon's heart,' said a fourth. 'Regin plans his death.'

Regin had followed Sigurd to the cave. Now that all was safe, he came up. He looked with greedy eyes on the treasure in the cave.

'Good,' he said. 'You have kept your promise well. Now light a fire and cook me the dragon's heart.'

Sigurd did what Regin ordered. While he was busy with the fire, it happened as the birds had said. Regin crept up on him and tried to kill him. But Sigurd was warned and ready. With the sword, Gram, he cut off Regin's head. Sigurd himself ate part of the dragon's flesh and took on some of Fafnir's power with it.

He loaded the treasure on to his father's horse, Grane, and went out into the world to seek his fortune. But even Sigurd, the hero, could not escape the curse that was on the treasure. He lost the woman he loved and came to his death by treachery in the end.

Looking at the story again
1. Who were Andvari and Hreidmar?
2. What had turned Fafnir into a dragon?
3. Who had brought up Sigurd?

4. What did Regin offer Sigurd as payment for killing Fafnir?
5. Which sentences tell you that it was not easy to mend the sword, Gram?
6. What did Odin look like when Sigurd met him?
7. Why was Fafnir difficult to kill?
8. How was Sigurd able to understand the language of birds?
9. How did Sigurd gain some of the dragon's power?
10. How did the curse on the treasure affect Sigurd?

Further questions
1. What is a wilderness?
2. What was Regin's real reason for looking after Sigurd?
3. Why did Sigurd not want the treasure for himself?
4. How do you know that the sword, Gram, was both very strong and very sharp?
5. What did the dying dragon mean when he said, '. . . there is a dwarf. His name is Regin. I leave you to him.'?
6. What is a smith? How does he shape iron? What is an anvil made of?

Things to do
1. Make a list of the things you think would be in Fafnir's treasure.
2. Write the story as if you were Regin.
3. Look at the picture and draw one of your own for this story.
4. Write a poem called 'The Hidden Dragon' or 'Listening to Birdsong'.
5. Have you ever visited a cave? Write a description of what it was like. Or, imagine what it was like in Fafnir's cave and describe that.
6. How, do you think, did the great sword, Gram, get broken in battle? Write your own story.
7. The tale can be divided up like this:
    (a) Regin asks Sigurd to kill Fafnir.
    (b) Sigurd is given good advice by Odin.
    (c) Sigurd kills Fafnir and talks to the dying dragon.
    (d) The birds warn Sigurd of Regin's treachery.
    (e) Sigurd kills Regin and rides off with the treasure.
Act out all or part of the story.

Glamr

In the Middle Ages, many sagas or long stories were written in Iceland and Norway. The saga of Grettir is one of them. The curse that Glamr put on him seemed to work. Because of that curse and his own violent nature, Grettir became an outcast and an outlaw. He fought and defeated other demons but in the end he met a violent death.

Pronunciation Guide

Thorhall	TORE-hal	Thurid	TOO-rid
Glamr	Glarm	Grettir	GRET-ear
Thorgaut	TORE-gowt	Jokull	YOKK-ull

Many years ago, in Iceland, there was a farmer, Thorhall. When he was growing old, bad luck came to him. Something started to kill his cattle. It could have been a bear or it could have been wolves. Thorhall's shepherds said that it was neither. They thought that Thorhall's farm was haunted. In the end he had a hard time getting any shepherd to work for him. When he first heard of Glamr, he was pleased.

Glamr was a huge fellow, heavy and strong, with staring eyes and hair like a wolf's. Thorall liked neither his looks nor his speech but Glamr agreed to work as a shepherd. That was the main thing.

'I'd better warn you,' Thorhall told him. 'People say that the farm is haunted.'

'Haunted, eh?' growled Glamr. 'That should make the place interesting.' He grinned evilly, showing teeth like a row of tombstones. He asked for high wages and said that he would come at the beginning of winter.

Glamr was good enough with the sheep. But he was surly and fierce and he had a harsh voice. That was not all of it. No one liked being near him for long. There was something very strange and frightening about Glamr.

It was the custom on Christmas Eve to eat nothing all day. But Glamr would have none of that. He demanded food and the frightened women gave it to him. He would not go to church with the rest of them, either. He went out into the wintry day with the sheep. Christmas Eve came and went and so did Christmas Day. But there was no sign of Glamr and they went out to look for him.

They found him dead and black with his eyes open. The snow round him was trodden and bloody. Tracks led away from the body. Glamr had fought with whatever was haunting Thorhall's farm and it had killed him. But he must have given it its death wound. It did not trouble Thorall's farm again.

Burying Glamr was a very strange business. They wanted to put him in the churchyard but he was too heavy to carry there. Even oxen could not drag him. As they could not bury him in holy ground they buried him where they had found him. Afterwards they piled stones on his grave.

But he did not lie quiet. Men began to see him here and there about the valley. He had grown bigger and he was a more frightening sight than he had been while alive. One man who saw him fell senseless with fear. People began to leave the valley for good. It was Thorhall, however, who suffered most.

His sheep and cattle were killed. After dark, Glamr was always about the farm. He broke into barns and they would hear him walking on the roof of Thorhall's house. Thorhall hired a man called Thorgaut who was fearless and strong. For a while things went better. It drew into summer when the nights were shorter and the noise of Glamr about the place did not seem to frighten Thorgaut at all. But summer led on into winter and then the time got round to Christmas again. Thorhall's wife grew nervous. On Christmas Eve Thorgaut was going out to look after the sheep. She reminded him of what had happened a year ago.

'Take care,' she warned him.

'Don't worry,' he laughed. 'It'll be time enough to worry if I don't come back. That troll doesn't frighten me.'

But he did not come back. When they went to look for him they found his body on the pile of stones over Glamr's grave. Not only was Thorgaut's neck broken but every other bone in his body as well.

Glamr was worse after that. His attacks drove nearly everyone out of the valley. In the end there were only Thorhall's family and his cowman left. One morning, later that winter, the cowman went out to the cows. They heard bellowing from the cow shed. When they got there, they found him dead. His back had been broken across a stone which separated one stall from another. Thorhall and his wife and daughter left the valley after that. Glamr roamed about and killed all the rest of the cattle.

But Thorhall wanted to try once more to build up his house and his farm. So they went back. In summer it was not too bad. But that winter Glamr killed Thorhall's daughter, Thurid.

Now Grettir was the strongest man in Iceland and he got to hear of Glamr. He told his uncle, Jokull, that he was going to visit Thorhall. Jokull, too, was a strong man and without fear but he shook his head.

'Evil things breed only evil,' he said. 'Fight with men, if you have to, Grettir, but not with trolls, not with the undead.'

It made no difference. Jokull could argue with him but Grettir had set his mind on helping Thorhall.

Even Thorhall warned him. 'You must have heard about Glamr,' he said. 'If you stay here, he'll have your horse, at least. I don't want to bring trouble on you.'

'I can get another horse,' Grettir said. 'I'll stay.'

Thorhall was glad of his company. It looked as though Grettir had brought him luck, too. Glamr did not trouble the farm that night or the next.

On the third morning, however, when they went outside, they found Grettir's horse dead in its stall. Big as it was, all its bones were broken. Thorhall repeated his warning.

'You had better leave,' he told Grettir.' If you wait here for Glamr, you'll be dead, too.'

'I deserve a good look at him in exchange for that horse,' said Grettir.

Night came and Thorhall went to bed. Grettir wrapped himself in a cloak, covering his head so that he looked out of the neck hole. The room was in a bad state, partly wrecked. The door had been pulled off and roughly mended. A light burned there all night. Grettir braced his feet against a post and waited.

Soon came a drumming and a clatter on the roof like a galloping horse. Up and down it went until the roof beams cracked. They heard someone jump down and a huge, ugly head poked in at the doorway. Grettir sat still.

Glamr came into the room and looked at the bundle in the cloak. He took hold of the cloth and pulled. Grettir resisted. Glamr tugged again, so strongly that the cloak tore in two. As Glamr stared stupidly at the piece in his hand, Grettir leaped up and grabbed him round the waist. Glamr took hold of his arms hard enough to make the muscles crack.

Up and down the room they went, wrestling together. Everything that came in their way was smashed. Glamr wanted to get outside. It would go worse for Grettir out there. Grettir fought hard but was drawn slowly to the door. He braced his feet against anything that would give him a grip. But Glamr was too strong for him. They came to the door and Glamr jerked Grettir towards him.

As he pulled, Grettir pushed, bracing his feet against a stone in the doorway. Glamr fell backwards. His shoulders struck the door and the roof came down. He crashed to the ground with Grettir on top of

him. Just then the moon came from behind a cloud and shone on Glamr's eyes. At the sight of them, Grettir could not move. All his strength left him.

'You were too eager to find me,' said Glamr. 'Now you will have my curse. Before you met me, your strength might have grown to twice what it is. Now you will never be a stronger man than you are this night. Your deeds have made you famous. After this, they will make you an outlaw. And, lastly, wherever you go from now on, you will see my eyes. After this night, you will hate to be alone.'

Then Grettir's weakness left him. He took his sword and cut off Glamr's head. When day came, he and Thorhall burned Glamr's body. When the ashes were cold, they put them in a leather bag. They buried what was left of Glamr far from the paths of men.

Looking at the story again
1. How did Thorhall feel about Glamr at first?
2. Why did people not like being near Glamr?
3. How did Glamr look when he came back from the dead?
4. How did Thorgaut die?
5. What made Thorhall and his wife and daughter leave the valley at last?
6. What advice did Jokull give Grettir?
7. How did Grettir bring Thorhall luck?
8. What noise told Thorhall and Grettir that Glamr was outside?
9. When the moon shone on Glamr's eyes what happened to Grettir?
10. How did Thorhall and Grettir make sure that Glamr would not come back from the dead again?

Further questions
1. How might Thorhall have known that Glamr was a strange creature at the first sight of him?
2. Glamr did not like going into a church. Why?
3. What was strange about the first burying of Glamr?
4. Why was Thorhall's wife nervous when Christmas time came round?
5. What points in the story show that Grettir was brave?
6. Why did Thorhall need a man to look after his sheep, in winter?

Things to do
1. Make a list of things that are supposed to bring bad luck.
2. Sheep bleat. What words describe the sounds that the following animals make? Bulls, lions, elephants, snakes, hyaenas, monkeys.
3. Look at the pictures and draw one of your own for this story.
4. Write about any special customs you have on Christmas Eve.
5. Write a poem called 'Moonlight' or 'Shepherd in Winter' or 'The Haunting Eyes'.
6. Tell Jokull's part of the story as if you were Jokull.
7. In play form, write the conversation Thorhall might have had with his wife when they were deciding to leave the valley.
8. The story can be divided up as follows:
    (a) Thorhall meets Glamr and hires him.
    (b) Glamr tells Thorhall's wife he is not going to church.
    (c) The finding of Glamr's body and the difficulty of burying it.
    (d) The hiring of Thorgaut.
    (e) Thorgaut talks to Thorhall's wife at Christmas and goes out.
    (f) The decision to leave the valley.
    (g) The return to the valley and the death of Thorhall's daughter.
    (h) Grettir talks to Jokull.
    (i) Thorhall warns Grettir of his danger.
    (j) The night in the hall and the killing of Glamr.
    (k) The second burial of Glamr.

Act out all or part of the story.

The Forest Ogre

This is a tale from India. There are stories like it in Africa and in the Southern States of America. In Africa they tell how the Spider-man was caught. He was a thief and the tribe from whom he had been stealing made a human figure and covered it with fresh rubber. When the Spider attacked it, he stuck to it and was held fast. In America, one of the stories about Brer Rabbit relates how his old enemy, Brer Fox, made a similar figure and coated it with tar. Brer Rabbit, annoyed that the figure would not talk to him, fought with it and was trapped by the tar. He was cunning enough, however, to escape from Brer Fox all the same.

This Indian story, called here, 'The Forest Ogre', has a more serious purpose behind it. The prince is really the Buddha, during one of his many lives on earth. He founded Buddhism, the religion of millions of people. The thunderbolt is religion or knowledge. The ignorance of the ogre has no power against such things.

For the substance of this tale we are indebted to Joseph Campbell's *The Hero With A Thousand Faces*, Bollingen Series, XVII (Princeton, N.J., Princeton University Press, 1972), pp. 85–9.

An old, wise man had spent many years in teaching a prince the arts of being a warrior and a good ruler. Now the prince's education was finished and it was time for him to return to his kingdom. On his way he came to a village. Beyond the village lay thick jungle and the prince would have to pass through it.

The villagers warned him of his danger. 'In that forest', the headman told him, 'is a fierce ogre. He can change his shape as he wishes and he kills and eats any traveller who comes in his way. Go round the forest. It will take you much longer to get home that way but at least you will get home alive.'

'Thank you for your advice,' said the prince politely. 'But, unfortunately, I cannot take it. My way must go through the forest. I

would fail as a warrior and as a prince, if I turned aside from the first test of my courage.'

So, sadly, the villagers had to let him go into the jungle. They watched him disappear into the trees.

The prince, however, was not sad. He had five weapons to use against the ogre and he had been well taught how to use them.

He had gone a good way into the green gloom of the jungle when suddenly all the forest noise fell silent. No monkeys chattered; the birds neither screeched nor whistled. Even the insects were still. There was only the sound of an oncoming tread that made the ground shake. As the prince stepped into a clearing, the ogre strode out to meet him.

The shape that the monster had taken was man-like. His head was huge and his blazing eyes seemed as big as the wheels of a bullock-wagon. His mouth was a savage beak and out of it grew tusks like those of an elephant. He was green all over like the weed on stagnant water and he was covered with thick, sticky hair. When he saw the prince, he roared with hunger and delight.

The prince was quite unafraid. He drew his bow and shot his arrows at the ogre. But the arrows could not get through the armour of hair and simply clung to it. The ogre shook himself so that they fell to the ground, leaving not the slightest mark on him. The same thing happened to the two spears which the prince hurled.

Then the prince drew his sword and aimed a two-handed blow at the monster. But that stuck fast, too, in the protective hair. As the snarling ogre jerked back, he pulled the sword from the prince's hand so that it hung on him harmlessly. With one sweep of his great hand, he plucked it from his hair and threw it far away into the trees.

Fearlessly, the prince took his club and aimed a blow with all his strength at his enemy's head. But the hair was a safe shield. The club, held fast, was also pulled from the prince's grip.

'Four of my weapons are shown to be useless,' said the prince as the creature began to growl in triumph. 'But I am practised in the use of five and I am not beaten yet.'

He advanced to do battle with his fists and feet. Each time he struck, however, he was held fast in the foul glue, first his right hand and then his left and then, one after the other, his feet. At the last, in desperation, thinking there must be a way of making some impression on the monster, the prince struck with his head. That, too, was imprisoned by the hair.

The ogre's massive hands were around the prince's ribs, ready to crush him. The sharp beak was opening ready to rip and eat.

'Wait!' cried the prince. 'You are in great danger.'

The ogre threw back his hideous head and laughed scornfully. When he was silent, the prince went on, 'If you eat me, you will be eating your own death.'

There was something so honest about the prince and his voice was so calm and serious that the ogre's clutch did not grow any fiercer. The great beak did not strike home.

'In my heart', said the prince, 'I carry a thunderbolt. If you eat my

body and take the thunderbolt into your own, it will tear you to pieces.'

The ogre believed him. He could feel that he had no ordinary being in his hands. The prince would tell him no lies. He let him go.

The prince was wise as well as brave. He spent many days in the forest, teaching the ogre human ways. The ogre came to see that his cruelty had been evil. He began to regret bitterly what he had done in the past. His earlier crimes lay very heavily on him. He left the jungle and went far away from mankind. He ate no living creature and thought constantly of what the prince had taught him.

The prince returned to his kingdom and no traveller along that path in the forest ever met danger there again.

Looking at the story again
1. What did the headman tell the prince about the ogre?
2. Why could the prince not take the headman's advice?
3. What signs showed the prince that he was getting near the ogre?
4. What did the ogre do when he saw the prince?
5. Why did the prince's arrows not harm the ogre?
6. How did the prince lose his sword?
7. What was the fifth weapon that the prince used?
8. What did the prince do when the ogre let him go?
9. What did the ogre do after his conversations with the prince?

Further questions
1. How do you know that the headman was kind-hearted?
2. The prince knew that the ogre was very powerful and heavy before he saw him. How?
3. What was the most frightening thing about the ogre?
4. Why did the ogre believe what the prince told him?
5. What was the prince's sixth weapon?

Things to do
1. Imagine what a walk through a jungle would be like and write a description.
2. Look at the picture and draw one of your own for the story.
3. Write the story as if you were one of the villagers.
4. The story can be divided up as follows:
    (a) The prince finishes his education and says goodbye to his teacher.
    (b) The headman warns the prince of his danger.
    (c) The prince fights with the ogre.
    (d) The prince talks to the ogre, showing him how evil he has been.

    Act out all or part of the story.

Killer Whale

The American Indians from the north Pacific coast region lived mainly by hunting and fishing. This is one of their legends. Dependent on animals for food, they felt very close to the animal world. In legends like this, animals are often like men. Sometimes an animal is the hero of the story. Totems, or figures of tribal gods, are often animal-like too.

The killer whale in this story seems both animal and human and greater in power than both kinds of being as well. Whale Hunter does not attack the monster directly. It may be that he knows that he stands little chance against superhuman powers. Perhaps these North American Indians admired intelligence and cunning in a hero more than strength.

Beowulf, too, battles under water. Gilgamesh, an Assyrian folk-hero, brings back the flower of youth from the ocean depths. The situation of some struggle under water occurs in more than one of these ancient tales. It would hardly have been possible for the different civilisations to have copied the idea from one another.

We found the material for this story in *North American Indian Mythology*, pp. 42–3, by Cottie Burland, Paul Hamlyn, 1973.

Whale Hunter was a medicine man and could make strong magic. He lived with his wife by the Great Water.

One day he killed a sea-otter and, while he was skinning it, he stained its bright fur with drops of blood. He told his wife to wash it and she put it under the waves of the sea shore and trod it gently with her feet to clean it. But the spirit of the otter was still in the skin. It floated away from the beach and carried the woman with it.

Within clear sight of land a whale came up from the depths and took Whale Hunter's wife on his back. In her fear she held on to the great fin of the whale's back and cried out. But before anyone could

reach her, the whale dived, carrying her down to his country at the bottom of the sea.

Whale Hunter called to Storm Rider, his friend and the two of them pushed their boat into the sea. Their paddles bit into the water and white foam frothed at the prow of the boat until they came to the spot where the great whale had dived.

In the boat Whale Hunter had a thin cord; it was very long and made of the toughest leather. He tied one end to the boat and, with the other in his hand, slipped over the side.

Down he sank, swimming ever deeper into the green light of the ocean. At last he came to the Country of the Killer Whale. It was like no land he had seen before. Strange plants grew there; the rocks were strangely shaped. Whale Hunter had never seen people before like those who lived in that country.

He gave them a friendly greeting and lifted his hand to show that he came in peace. But, though they greeted him, too, they turned their heads from side to side, listening to his voice and he could see that they were blind.

'The curse of not-seeing is on our tribe,' they told him. 'Our eyes are sealed from birth.'

When he looked closely, however, he saw that a skin was growing over their eyes. It seemed to him that he could heal them and he told them so. Excited but doubtful, they let him try.

Delicately with his knife he cut the skin that kept them blind. He dusted each wound immediately with magic powder that he took from his medicine pouch and there was neither bleeding nor pain. They were overjoyed to be able to see, and promised him their friendship and help for as long as he lived. As well as they could, they directed him to the lodge of the Killer Whale and he proceeded on his journey.

He had walked far among strange sights when he came on an old man who was complaining bitterly to himself.

'What is your trouble?' asked Whale Hunter.

'My master the Killer Whale ordered me to cut wood for the fire that heats his lodge and boils the water. Now I shall be well beaten. It may be that I shall lose my life. I have been using this stone wedge to split the logs and I have broken it.'

'Give it to me,' said Whale Hunter. He took the broken pieces and he put them in his mouth. Then he blew on them and spoke secret words of power over them, sprinkling them with magic powder. When he showed the wedge to the old man it was whole again and as good, if not better, than it had ever been.

The old man was surprised but grateful. The wood he had chopped was for Whale Hunter's wife. It was her job to build the fire in Killer Whale's lodge. In due course the wives of Killer Whale would work their magic on her. She would change into a magical being, like the Killer Whale and his wives, who was at times like a woman and at other times like a whale.

'Will you help me, as I've helped you?' asked Whale Hunter when the old man had finished telling him all this.

'I cannot go against my master,' said the old man. 'I am old and frightened and not fit now for much more than getting wood and carrying water. I dare not help you to set your wife free. I must stay in this land. If he saw that I helped her to escape, the Killer Whale would have my life.'

'What I want is not a big thing,' said Whale Hunter. 'When you carry in the buckets of water for the lodge as you always do, put them near the fire. And tell my wife to build the fire high so that it burns hot. Will you do it?'

'I see no harm in that,' said the old man. 'She must make a good fire anyway.'

He carried in the buckets of water and ranged them round the blazing fire. Whale Hunter took a long stick and hid himself by the door. When he saw the heat shimmer over the stones of the fireplace, he took his stick and quickly overturned the buckets. The water hissed on the hot stones and glowing logs, turning immediately into steam. Thick clouds of white mist filled the place and the wives of the Killer Whale shouted in anger and alarm.

In the confusion, Whale Hunter sprang in, grabbed his wife by the wrist and got her out of the door. But the Killer Whale saw them go through the foggy steam and came after them. Whale Hunter took more of the magic powder from his belt and threw it over the Killer Whale. The creature changed its shape and began to grow in size until it could not get through the door.

Whale Hunter and his wife went as fast as they could back the way that Whale Hunter had come. In the lodge, the wives of Killer Whale threw water on their husband so that he shrank in size until at last they could all get out of the lodge. They travelled far more quickly than Whale Hunter and rapidly began to overtake him and his wife.

They might have caught them, if the people whom Whale Hunter had cured of blindness had not helped. They set traps for the Killer Whale and his wives. This delayed them enough for Whale Hunter to find the cord that hung down from the boat. They pulled on it as a signal to Storm Rider and he hauled them up and back into the boat. Whale Hunter threw out the last of the magic powder to confuse the whales and he and his wife and Storm Rider reached land safely.

Looking at the story again

1. What made the skin of the sea-otter float out to sea?
2. Whale Hunter met some strange people. What caused their blindness?
3. Why did their wounds not bleed when Whale Hunter cured them?
4. How did Whale Hunter mend the broken wedge?
5. What was going to happen to Whale Hunter's wife?
6. Why would the old man not help Whale Hunter's wife to escape?
7. What happened when Whale Hunter overturned the buckets?
8. Why did Whale Hunter throw magic powder over the Killer Whale?
9. Who delayed the Killer Whale and his wives long enough for Whale Hunter to find the cord and the boat?

Further questions

1. How do you know that Whale Hunter and Storm Rider paddled their boat very quickly?
2. What elements of life under the sea in the story are like life on the earth above it? What elements are different?
3. In what other story in this book does the hero use a cord or thread?
4. What things in the story show you that Whale Hunter was clever?
5. Why might the Killer Whale have needed a fire?
6. Seals are killed on the British coast to protect the fishing industry. Why is this practice different from Whale Hunter's killing of animals?

Things to do

1. The Killer Whale's home is described as a lodge. Write your own description of what you imagine it looked like.
2. Look at the pictures and draw one of your own for this story.
3. Invent some Red Indian names such as Goal-Scorer or He-Who-Laughs-Easily for your friends.
4. Find out about and write the story of Jonah. Do you think it could have happened? Why?

5. Whale Hunter relies more on intelligence than fighting power. What other heroes can you name who are like him?

6. The idea of a race of completely blind people occurs in a story by H. G. Wells, *The Country of the Blind*. What sort of difficulties might such people face and how might they overcome them?

7. Making it as vivid as possible as regards his size, write a description of Killer Whale in his form as a whale.

8. If you were a Red Indian medicine man, how would you use your powers?

9. You have the power to change yourself into an animal, fish or bird. You can, of course, change back to being yourself. Write an account of what you do, showing why you enjoy being that particular creature.

10. The story can be divided up as follows;
    (a) Whale Hunter's wife washes the skin and is carried out to sea.
    (b) Whale Hunter sees her carried off by the Killer Whale and follows.
    (c) He journeys down into the sea and meets the blind people.
    (d) He talks to the old man.
    (e) He rescues his wife.
    (f) The flight from the Killer Whale and his wives and the return to land.

Act out all or part of the story.

The Husband with Five Heads

You may recognise something familiar about this story though it comes from Africa. It is a bit like some of our own folk stories, such as 'The Frog Prince' or 'Beauty and the Beast'. This tale, however, seems to be trying to teach a lesson and the monster itself meets a better fate than most monsters in this book do.

We have adapted this from one of the stories in Kathleen Arnott's book, *African Myths and Legends*, Oxford University Press, 1972.

Long ago, in an African village, there lived a man with two daughters. He felt it was time that they were married.

He searched by water and by land until he found a tribe whose chief wanted a wife. Though he did not see the chief, the father struck a bargain and promised one of his daughters as a wife.

Now, the elder daughter was a proud girl. When the father returned home, she said, 'I will marry this chief. I will leave at once.'

'Wait a bit,' said the father. 'You can't go alone. That is not the custom. You must take people with you. A woman who goes to be married goes with a singing procession. That has always been the custom.'

'It isn't my custom,' said the elder daughter and she left.

On her travels she met a mouse who offered to show her the way to the chief's village.

'You?' said the elder daughter. 'I can't waste my time talking to mice. Get off with you!' And she strode on, nearly treading on the mouse, which wished her bad luck. She then met a frog which also offered to direct her. She was equally rude to the frog. She met a herd boy who greeted her politely and asked her if she had any food to give him.

'No,' said the elder daughter. 'And if I had twenty men with me loaded with food, you certainly wouldn't get any.' She tossed her head and marched on.

Then she came across a very old woman.

'I know you and I know where you are going,' said the old woman. 'I will give you some good advice.'

'When I need advice, I will ask for it,' said the elder daughter but the old woman told her just the same.

'Shortly you will reach some trees,' she said. 'They are enchanted. You will hear them laughing. Don't show surprise and, whatever you do, don't laugh. Just hurry past.'

'Do you expect me to believe that?' said the girl.

'Then you will find a leather bag full of milk,' the old woman continued. 'Do not touch the bag and do not drink the milk. Finally you will meet a man who is carrying his own head. He will offer you water to drink. Do not speak to him and do not touch the water.'

'What rubbish!' said the elder daughter, and hurried on.

But she did come to a group of trees which laughed. Though she felt they were not showing her enough respect, she could not help laughing, too. Giggling, she walked on. The heat and the long journey were making her thirsty. She was pleased when she found a skin bag full of milk on the trail. It was cool and delicious and she drank it all.

There was, however, still quite a long way to go and she soon got thirsty again. When she met a headless man who offered her water she was so relieved that she did not bother about his looks. She drank all the water he could give her.

When at last she came in sight of some huts in the distance, she also met a young girl who told her that she had reached the village she was looking for.

'But,' said the young girl, 'I wouldn't go straight into the village along this path. That will be unlucky. Go round the village and enter it another way.'

'I've walked for miles already and I'm not going to waste my time wandering round and round those huts now,' said the elder daughter and she walked straight down the path and into the village. She sat down and told the women who gathered about her that she had come to marry their chief.

'Where are your attendants?' one of the women asked. 'We should have heard them singing as you approached.'

'Oh, I don't bother my head with things like that!' said the elder daughter scornfully.

They said nothing to this but they did tell her that, if she was going to be the chief's bride, she would have to get his meal ready. She would have to prove that she could cook.

She could see that there was nothing else for it so, resentfully, she ground the grain to make bread. Because she did her work so badly, the bread, when it was baked, was full of husks and bits of stone from the mill wheels she had used to grind the grain.

The elder daughter did not care. She sat lazily in the chief's hut with the bread beside her and thought how important she would be when she was married.

Evening came. Then a great wind sprang up and rushed into the hut. The elder daughter jumped to her feet. But the wind was not so frightening as the being she had come to marry. She screamed when she saw him. Not only was he a huge snake but he had five heads. He hissed at her to give him food but when he tasted the bread he hissed even louder with rage.

'You think you're fit to be my wife?' he accused her. 'You're fit for nothing!' And he struck her with his tail and killed her.

When the news came to the father he was distressed when his younger daughter still wanted to marry the chief. But she said she had to go because of his promise, so he let her leave.

Her friends went with her and sang happily to bring her on her way. She, too, met a mouse but she talked politely to it and thanked it for showing her the right path. Later she met an old woman who directed her correctly at a spot where the trail forked. Again the younger daughter thanked her for the advice and followed it. Then the party came across a rabbit. It stopped the younger daughter and told her that near the village she was seeking she would meet a young girl.

'Speak to her courteously,' said the rabbit. 'And do what she tells you to do.'

'I will,' said the younger daughter.

'You will be given grain to grind and you will be asked to make bread for the chief. Do that as well as you can,' the rabbit told her. 'When you see the chief, you will be afraid. But do not cry out or show your fear.'

The younger daughter thanked it and said that she would do what she had been told.

Sure enough, she met the young girl who told her how she should enter the village. The younger daughter treated her with politeness. When the younger daughter was asked to make bread for the chief, she was careful to see that the grain was properly ground and the bread properly baked.

Like her sister she sat in the hut with the bread beside her and like her sister she trembled when she heard and felt the rushing of the great wind.

But when she saw the monster she was to marry, she did not cry out. Even when the five savage heads swayed above her, hissing, she showed no sign of fear.

This time, however, the five-headed snake ate the bread with enjoyment and not with anger. When he had finished, he asked the younger daughter to be his wife.

She kept her voice steady and said she would.

As soon as she had spoken the words, the snake-skin disappeared as the monster changed its shape. The chief was a handsome young man again. The younger daughter had broken the spell which held him.

The village rejoiced to have their chief restored to them in his proper form. The marriage was celebrated with ceremonies that went on for days. The chief and his wife ruled over the village with justice and lived happily together for very many years.

Looking at the story again

1. How far did the father search for a husband?
2. What was the usual custom when a girl went to be married?
3. What did the mouse wish the elder daughter?
4. How many beings altogether tried to give advice to the elder daughter? Name each one. Don't forget the young girl.
5. What did she do when she found the skin bag full of milk?
6. How did the elder daughter feel as she ground the grain for the chief's bread?
7. What happened when evening came?
8. The elder daughter went alone to the chief's village. Who went with the younger daughter?
9. How many beings gave the younger daughter their advice?

10. What happened when the younger daughter agreed to marry the snake?

Further questions
1. Name three things that show you that the elder daughter was not only proud but rude and self-willed as well.
2. How might we guess at the beginning that there was something strange about the chief?
3. What might the trees have been laughing about?
4. Which action of the elder daughter, in your opinion, was the most foolish and why?
5. Why did the younger daughter feel that she had to go and marry the chief?
6. What attitude towards women does the tale show? Do you agree with it?

Things to do
1. How did the young chief come to be turned into the snake? Invent your own story.
2. Look at the picture and draw one of your own to the story.
3. This is the only tale in this book which has a woman as the chief character. Re-tell an old tale or invent one of your own for young children which has a heroine and not a hero.
4. Write a description of what the African village would have looked like.
5. What marriage customs do we have in this country which might seem strange to a non-European?
6. The story can be divided up as follows:
    (a) The father discusses the marriage with the villagers.
    (b) He returns home and talks to his daughters.
    (c) The elder daughter sets out and meets the various beings who give advice. She makes the bread.
    (d) She meets the snake-husband.
    (e) The younger daughter persuades her father to let her go.
    (f) She, too, meets the various advisers and makes bread.
    (g) The meeting with the snake husband.
    (h) The marriage celebrations.
Act out all or part of the story.

The Demons

Ivan, in this tale from Russia, is a slightly different kind of hero. He is a very ordinary man but with his bravery and his cunning he can look after himself. You may have come across some of his tricks before in similar stories. There is a German folk-tale, 'The Valiant Little Tailor' where a tailor outwits a giant rather as Ivan outwits the demons.

We took the elements of this story and the next from Charles Downing's book, *Russian Tales and Legends*, Oxford University Press, 1960.

Ivan had been a soldier in the Russian army for twenty-five years. On his last day the sergeant came up to him.

'Ivan,' he said. 'The Tsar doesn't need you any more. Your time's up. You're finished. You're free. Go home.'

Ivan set off home. He had his gun, a bag to carry on his back and three very dry biscuits. It did not take him long to eat two of these.

'It's not much to show for twenty-five years' service to the Tsar,' he said to himself. He was sitting under a tree with the last biscuit in his hand. 'A gun, a bag and a few biscuits. It's a long way home, too, without money. I wonder if my old mother and father are still alive.'

Just before he could bite into the biscuit, a beggar came up and asked for food.

'Take it.' Ivan handed him the biscuit. 'A poor old fellow like you needs it more than I do. All you can do is beg. After twenty-five years as a soldier, I know a few more tricks than that.'

His kindness brought him luck. Later that day he saw some wild geese on a lake. He shot three and took them to the inn in the nearby small town. The landlord took two as payment. He cooked the third for the soldier and gave him soup and bread and wine and fruit as well.

'Things are looking up,' said the soldier, after he had eaten. 'This seems a rich village. There are some fine big houses here. Why is that one across the road empty?'

'Demons,' said the landlord.

'Demons?' asked the soldier.

'That's what I said,' the landlord told him. 'That house is full of demons. Anyone who spends the night there ends up dead. Two or three have tried it. In the morning, all that was left of them was a heap of clean white bones.'

'Nasty,' said the soldier, drinking his wine.

'The house belongs to a merchant,' the landlord went on. 'He'd pay good money to have the place free of demons.'

'Would he?' said Ivan.

He went to see the merchant and told him that he would spend a night in the house of demons. The merchant, who was a kind-hearted man, shook his head and warned Ivan of the danger.

'Old soldiers never die,' Ivan told him. 'Get me some candles, some nuts and a nice round new cheese and I'll rid you of the demons tonight. We can talk about payment tomorrow.'

So, as darkness fell, Ivan was alone in the house with his candles lit and the nuts and cheese in his soldier's pack beside him. He heard a scuffling and a chattering. A head with horns and bright red eyes poked round the door.

'Aha!' cried the demon. 'I thought so. There's a man here again. We'll all eat well tonight.' Ivan heard other demons growling and snarling. There was the rattle of hooves and claws in the corridor.

'Stop that noise!' he shouted. 'Don't hang about outside there. Come in!'

Feeling a little surprised, the demons crowded into the room.

'You can't talk to us like that,' said the biggest one, the leader. 'We're demons. We eat men like you right down to their bones.'

'Don't talk daft,' said Ivan. 'I'm more than a match for any demon.'

'Are you?' said the leader. The other demons crowded closer, showing their teeth.

'We'll have a few tests of skill,' said Ivan calmly. 'That'll show you who is best. Can you get water from a stone?'

'What?' said the leader of the demons. 'Water from a stone? I suppose so.'

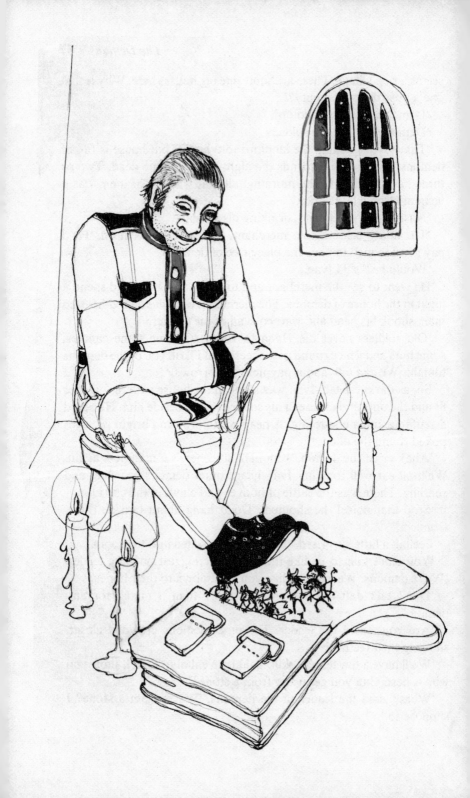

'Prove it,' said Ivan. One of the smaller demons ran outside and brought the leader a pebble.

'Watch,' said the demon and squeezed the pebble. It crumbled to dust but no water came from it.

'That's very poor,' said the soldier. 'Now—*you* watch.' He took the stony-looking cheese out of his bag and gripped it until water from it dripped on the floor. All the demons chattered together. They were impressed.

'That was too difficult for you,' said the soldier. 'Try something simpler. Can you crack nuts in your teeth? Like this?' He took a couple of nuts from his bag, cracked them and ate them.

'Of course I can do that,' said the leader of the demons, growing angry. 'Give me a nut and I'll show you.'

But the soldier handed out bullets from his bag. Neither the leader nor any of the other demons could crack bullets in their teeth.

'You're a feeble lot,' said the soldier. 'Are you sure you're demons?' In a great rage they roared that they were.

'A real demon can grow as big as a giant or as small as a beetle,' said the soldier. 'Can you all do that?'

They snarled at him that they could.

'Never mind about growing as big as giants, then,' said Ivan. 'There isn't room for that in here. Let's see if you can become as small as beetles and creep into a small space. This will do.' He threw his empty bag on the floor. 'I bet you can't all get into that.'

In a second all the demons had shrunk in size and rushed angrily into the bag. In the next second the soldier had strapped it up safe and tight. Whistling, he threw it under the bed and went to sleep.

In the morning he went to the town blacksmith and put the bag on the anvil.

'Give that a good hammering for me,' he said. 'Never mind the noise it makes.'

And the blacksmith, who was a helpful sort of man, hammered until the sweat ran down his face.

'That's enough,' said the soldier and the smith stopped. 'Can you hear me in there?' he shouted. The demons howled and groaned that they could.

'If you promise never to come anywhere near this town again,' he said, 'I'll let you out.'

'Agreed!' they screamed. 'You have our promise.' He was just going to undo the bag when a thought struck him.

'Wait a bit,' he said. 'I've earned something from you. I'll let you all out except your leader, the big one. He must pay a ransom.'

'Anything,' roared the leader. 'But no more hammering.'

'Right you are,' said the soldier and undid one strap. The demons leaped out and were off down the road like bullets from a gun. They disappeared in a cloud of dust. The soldier carefully strapped the bag up again before the leader could escape.

One demon was back almost at once, carrying a leather bag.

'What's that?' asked the soldier.

'The ransom, sir,' said the demon.

'That's not much of a ransom,' the soldier said.

'Try it!' shouted the leader of the demons from inside his prison. 'Wish for anything and you'll find it in the bag.'

'I wouldn't mind a few bottles of beer,' said the soldier. He opened the leather bag and there they were. 'I'll accept the ransom,' he said. He let the leader of the demons go and he was off down the road like a flash of lightning.

The soldier looked at the leather bag of wishes and drank his beer. 'It has a lot of possibilities,' he said. There was a crow on a nearby roof. 'Crow!' he said. 'In the bag!' And the next moment, the surprised crow found itself a prisoner. The soldier let it go and went off to see the merchant. The merchant was very pleased to have his house back and free of demons. He offered the soldier a lot of money. But the soldier refused it. The leather bag of wishes was all the payment he needed. The merchant, however, did insist on the soldier attending a great feast given in his honour.

When the soldier got home he found both his old parents alive and well. The demon's wishing bag made them all rich. But no matter how big his farm grew or however much money he had, the soldier kept the bag in a very safe place. A thing like that, he said, was always very useful.

Looking at the story again

1. What reward did Ivan get for serving twenty-five years in the army?
2. How did his kindness to the beggar bring him luck?

3. What had happened to everyone who spent the night in the house of demons?
4. How did the demons feel when Ivan ordered them to come into his room?
5. What happened when the leader of the demons tried to squeeze water from his pebble?
6. What promise did the demons make to the soldier?
7. What ransom did the leader of the demons pay?
8. What happened when the soldier got home?

Further questions
1. What points in the story show you that Ivan was kind and brave and clever?
2. What things show you that the demons are really rather stupid?
3. Why did the soldier not need the merchant's money?
4. Do you think that the demons would keep their promise not to come back to the village? Why?
5. What shows you that the merchant was a fair-minded man?

Things to do
1. Look at the picture and draw one of your own for the story.
2. In what ways is this story different from the others in this book?
3. Ivan was taken prisoner while in the army. Write a short play to describe how he escaped from his enemies.
4. Describe the events in the story as if you were one of the demons.
5. How many words can you find which mean 'trick'? How many words, like 'Tsar', can you find which mean 'king'?
6. The story can be divided up like this:
   (a) Ivan leaves the army.
   (b) He meets the beggar and shoots the wild geese.
   (c) He eats at the inn and talks to the landlord.
   (d) He talks to the merchant.
   (e) He tricks the demons.
   (f) He visits the blacksmith and receives the wishing bag.
   (g) His return home.
   Act out all or part of the story.

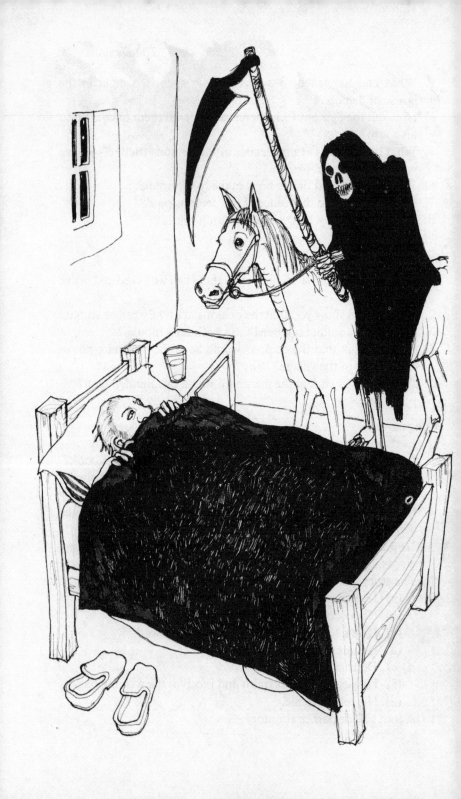

Death

Ivan was right. The bag was very useful. He married and started a family. As the years went by, his children grew up strong and healthy.

Then Ivan fell ill. He lay in bed feeling worse every moment. He closed his eyes but he could not sleep. When he opened them, there was a horse in the room. It was ghostly white and very thin. But it was not as thin as its rider. He was a skeleton and he carried a scythe.

'Ivan,' said the skeleton. 'My name is Death and I have come for you.'

'I'm not ready for death yet,' said the soldier.

'Oh, yes, you are,' said Death. 'Come along.'

Ivan was not so ill that he could not move. In a flash he was out of the bed and had opened the cupboard where he kept the wishing bag.

'Death!' he ordered. 'In the bag!'

And Death and his scythe and his pale horse were safely in the bag. Ivan felt better at once. He felt strong enough to take a good long walk. He went up a high mountain and hung the bag on the branch of a fir tree. He was pretty sure that no one else would ever get up there.

He was right about that, too. Death did not trouble him any more. His illness left him and he felt very fit. He no longer had the use of the bag. That did not matter much. The farm did well and he grew richer. But there was another thing that he had not thought about. With Death out of the way up the mountain, no one in the whole world ever died.

It was an old woman who made the soldier realise what he had done. He met her struggling along the road and complaining.

'I've lived too long, soldier,' she told him. 'My bones ache and my strength has left me. For people like me, Death comes as a welcome rest. You did wrong to make him a prisoner like that. Be careful that God doesn't punish you for it.'

'I didn't think about that,' said the soldier. 'I'm sorry.' When he thought about it he saw he had made a mistake. He had had all those extra years of life and others had suffered. He was a fair man so he got the bag from the tree. Then he went home, said goodbye to his family and opened the bag.

'You can come out, Death,' he said. 'I'm ready for you now.'

But the moment Death got out of the bag he jumped on his horse and galloped away.

'This is the last you'll see of me, soldier!' he shouted. 'You're far too tricky for me to deal with.'

It worried the soldier. What the old woman had said about God was on his mind.

'She was right,' he told himself. 'We all owe God a death. I've cheated him out of my soul for all these years. I'd better put that right.' He decided to go down into Hell first. 'They'll wash me free of all my sins down there,' he told himself. 'They'll use liquid fire to do it, I suppose. But an old soldier is used to hardship. When it's over, I can go to God free of sin.'

So he went down to the terrible gates of Hell.

'Let me in!' he shouted. 'I've come to be cleaned of my sins.'

'Who is it?' asked one of the demons, looking through the gate.

'It's me, Ivan,' said the soldier.

As soon as the demon recognised him, it screamed aloud in fear.

'Go away!' it yelled. 'I'm not letting you in here. I've heard about you.'

The Devil came to see what the matter was. He had heard about Ivan, too.

'Go away!' he roared. 'We know about you and the tricks you get up to. We don't want your sort down here.'

Ivan saw that it was going to be very difficult to get into Hell.

'I'll strike a bargain,' he called. 'Set free two hundred of those poor souls you're torturing in there. Then I'll go away and stop bothering you.'

'Two hundred?' called the Devil in great relief. 'Take two hundred and fifty.' And he set free the souls of two hundred and fifty dead people. They were very pleased to get out of Hell.

The soldier marched his company then up to the Gates of Heaven.

'Who's there?' called St Peter, looking out.

'It's me,' said Ivan. 'And a few others with me.'

'I know you,' said St Peter. 'We've heard all about you and your wishing bag. You're not coming in here. There's no telling what trouble you'd give us with your bag and your tricks.'

Ivan could see that it was no use trying to talk his way into Heaven.

'Wait a bit,' he cried, as St Peter was turning away. 'I've got two hundred and fifty poor souls out here. They don't know any tricks. They haven't any wishing bags. You can safely let them in.'

St Peter looked them all over and then said that he would let them in.

'Here, Stefan!' said Ivan to one of the souls. 'Take this bag. As soon as you're inside Heaven, say, "Ivan, the soldier! In the bag!"'

The soul of the dead man agreed, took the bag and ran into Heaven, shouting for joy. Unfortunately, as soon as he got inside the Gates, he was so pleased that he threw the bag away and forgot all about Ivan.

Time means nothing outside the Gates of Heaven. Ivan waited around Up There for a year or two. But St Peter always kept a careful eye on him and would not let him in. At last Ivan shrugged his shoulders and went whistling on his way back to earth.

So Ivan, the soldier, never got into either Heaven or Hell. He is probably working on his farm or walking the roads of Russia to this day. But let us not be too sorry for him. He is a man who can obviously look after himself.

Looking at the story again

1. What did Death's horse look like?
2. How did Ivan feel when Death and his horse were in the bag?
3. Who made Ivan realise what he had done?
4. What happened when Ivan let Death out of the bag?
5. Why did the soldier go down into Hell?
6. How did the Devil feel about him?
7. What payment did Ivan take for going away from the gates of Hell?
8. Why would St Peter not let him into Heaven?
9. What trick did Ivan play to try to get into Heaven?
10. What happened to him in the end?

Further questions

1. What shows you that Ivan could think quickly when he was in danger?
2. Why was the old woman not pleased when she found that she could not die?
3. Why did the demon scream when it saw Ivan?
4. What things in the story show that Ivan did not always think of himself first?
5. Should we feel sorry for him? Why?

Things to do

1. Write a poem called 'Moment of Fear' or 'The Wanderer'.
2. Copy the picture or draw your own illustration to the story.
3. Write the story as if you were Death himself.
4. Explain why Death carries a scythe.
5. Invent a way for Ivan to get into Heaven and tell the story.
6. The story can be divided up like this:
   (a) Death comes for Ivan and is tricked.
   (b) Ivan meets the old woman.
   (c) Death runs away and Ivan decides to go down to Hell.
   (d) Ivan outside the gates of Hell.
   (e) Ivan outside the Gates of Heaven.

   Act out all or part of the story.

Thinking back

All the heroes in this book faced death. Who was the bravest? Who was the cleverest? Who was the strongest? Which one would you like to have been?

All the heroes had help from weapons or equipment. Which was the most useful?

Some of the heroes were helped by friends. Which friend gave the most help?

Which of the stories did you find most interesting and why?

Which pieces of work arising from these stories gave you most pleasure to do?